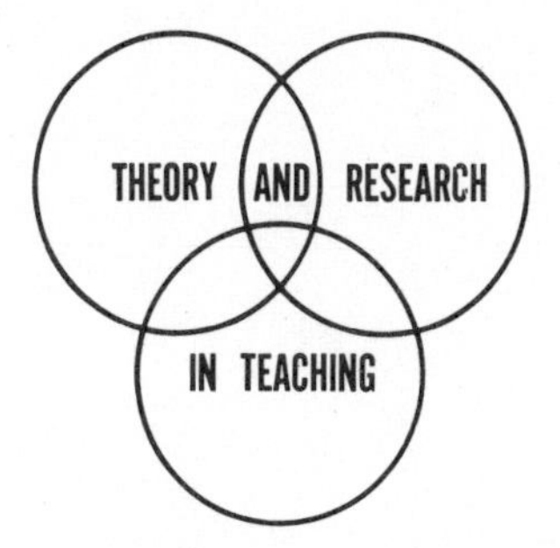

Teachers College, Columbia University
Arno A. Bellack, editor

Recent years have witnessed a resurgence of interest on the part of educational researchers in the teaching process. Volumes in the *Theory and Research in Teaching* series report significant studies of instructional procedures in a variety of educational settings, at various organizational levels in the schools, and in many of the subjects included in the curriculum. These studies present fresh perspectives on teaching both to educational researchers and to practitioners in the schools.

Quantitative Analysis of Structure in Teaching

O. ROGER ANDERSON

TEACHERS COLLEGE PRESS
Teachers College, Columbia University
New York

Library of Congress Catalog Card Number: 76-150210

Manufactured in the United States of America

Foreword

Although the concept of "structure" as related to the organization of knowledge in the curriculum has gained wide currency in educational theory, little attention has been given by researchers to the development of a conception of "structure" as related to subject matter communicated in the teaching process. The pioneering investigation reported by Dr. Anderson in *Structure in Teaching* (1969) was one of the first attempts to formulate a theory of teaching in which the concept of structure played a central role. The present volume, based on his more recent studies of the teaching of science, extends and refines the theory and methods developed in the earlier work.

Dr. Anderson's investigations are significant additions to the growing body of research on teaching, for they focus attention on aspects of the instructional process that have been largely ignored by other researchers. Teachers cannot teach without teaching *something*, and the analyses presented in this volume begin to shed light on the relationships between the serial ordering and organization of subject matter communicated in the classroom and the acquisition of meaningful verbal material by students.

ARNO A. BELLACK

Preface

Subsequent to the publication of *Structure in Teaching: Theory and Analysis* (1969), sufficient progress has been made in the refinement and extension of the theory and methods to warrant this second book. Some additional information is presented on the relationship of structure in teaching to acquisition of knowledge. The roles of contiguity and commonality (having elements in common) are discussed as they pertain to relatedness among discourse units in a communication. The interaction between commonality and progression (the rate at which new information is added) is discussed. Classifications of transitions between major topics in a communication and their empirical identification are described and illustrated using transcripts of classroom discourse. Considerable advancement has been made in the use of Kinetograms as analytical tools in deciphering the structure of a communication. Some careful tests have been made to determine the reliability and robustness of the quantitative methods employing coefficients of kinetic structure. The serial comparison method of analyzing structure in a communication has been applied to classroom discourse through the use of computer programs. This advance marks a departure from previous practice where only programmed lessons were amenable to such an analysis.

There are several people whose assistance and encouragement I wish to acknowledge. Mr. Ralph Kilsheimer and other members of the Teachers College Computer Center were very helpful during the period when I was writing computer programs. I extend particular appreciation and thanks to Marjorie Muehlke, Liberty Mhlanga, Arnold Trindade, and Tom White, who as members of my seminar assisted in coding and analyzing transcripts.

O.R.A.

Contents

Charts

Figures

Tables

Quantitative Analysis of Structure in Teaching

CHAPTER I

Theory

A theory of structure in verbal communication previously presented in *Structure in Teaching: Theory and Analysis* (*3*) * will be further elaborated and applied to the analysis of classroom communications in this volume.

A Theory of Structure in Learning and Communication

The theory is built upon certain biological and psychological principles. The following are its basic assumptions:

1. The natural environment favored the evolution of organisms possessing receptors and nerve networks sensitive to periodic stimuli.

2. During human ontogeny, visual scanning of the environment produces a succession of images on the retina of the eye wherein each image contains some elements in common with contiguous images. These experiences predispose the organism to anticipate common properties or shared elements in successive stimuli.

3. Language and thought are products of these genetic influences. They are both in part serial processes wherein contiguous units hold elements in common.

4. Acquisition of verbal material is enhanced when contiguous verbal units (statements) in a communication contain identical verbal elements or hold other properties in common.

* Italic numbers in parentheses refer to numbered items in the list of References, pages 91–93.

A major premise of the theory is that periodicity in environmental stimuli is a major selecting factor in evolution whereby the complex behavior of advanced organisms can be partially understood. The discussion here of this theory of behavior will include: phylogenetic (evolutionary) parameters, ontogenetic (developmental) parameters, and the relationships of these parameters to human learning and communication.

Phylogenetic Parameters

The principles of natural selection and organismic adaptation have been widely applied in biology to explain the forms and functions of contemporary living organisms. The premise basic to these principles is that certain properties of the environment favor survival of well-adapted organisms but result in death and recession of less successful forms. These fundamental biological principles of environmental selection and the survival of the best-fitted are the organic bases of the theory of behavior to be developed here.

The physical environment contains many periodic phenomena. The most obvious is the rotation of the earth producing dark and light cycles. The motions of oceanic waves and tides are additional examples of periodic spatial events which must have developed early in the history of our planet. The electromagnetic radiation of sunlight is further evidence of a periodic form of energy. Modern physical science has gained increasing evidence that light consists of discrete units (photons) whose energy is directly related to the frequency of their associated oscillating electromagnetic field.

Environmental periodicity or repetitiveness will be used to explain the origin of photoreceptors containing chromophores sensitive to electromagnetic radiation and the induction of complex nervous systems in higher animals.

At the beginning of phylogeny, certain photosensitive compounds capable of absorbing electromagnetic radiation were selected as part of the organic development of primitive living forms. These pigmented individuals, being potentially phototactic, had a higher probability of survival by locomotion to regions of optimum light intensity where primary food producers were available. The sensory pigments also allowed these simple living forms to avoid regions of lethally high radiation. Thus, early in evolutionary development, the periodic energy available in the environment favored the survival of photosensitive primitive living forms.

At a very early stage in phylogeny, the inclusion of chromophores constituted a selection function of the environment. The evidence for an early phylogenetic acquisition of chromophores in living forms has come from biochemical analyses of extant organisms. All phototactic organisms, from the simple unicellular protozoan to mammals, including man, contain a common photoreceptive compound. Beta-carotene and its derivatives, vitamins A_1 and A_2, are ubiquitously distributed in photosensitive living forms. Moreover, the presence of these compounds in unicellular organisms is evidence that their inclusion was an early adaptation.

The formation of carotenoproteins by the adsorption of retinene (vitamin A_1 aldehyde) on various proteins produces lipo-proteins with a wide range of absorption maxima (*22; 25*). Carotenes have been identified in the photoreceptors of protozoa (*14;* 9), annelids (*24*), molluscs (*16*), arthropods (*35; 17*), fish (*6; 31*), amphibians (*11; 32*), reptiles (33), birds (*34*), and mammals (*11; 12; 7; 30*, p. 224). The early selection of this compound, therefore, appears to have persisted throughout phylogeny as continuous evidence of the critical role of periodic radiation in natural selection.

These and various other biological data clearly point toward the fundamental role of periodicity in natural phenomena producing profound physiological effects in living organisms (2). Indeed, it has been shown that diurnal cycles of light and darkness form the temporal cues for the physiological rhythms in invertebrates. Cell division in Euglena occurs predominantly in the dark (*21*). Moreover, clear evidence is available to show that this cytokinetic periodicity is induced by light and dark cycles (*21; 18*, p. 324). Animals as well as plants depend on the photoperiod as a signal for changes in annual reproductive cycles (25). Diurnal fluctuations in temperature associated with periodic irradiation from the sun have been cited as critical factors in the early phylogenetic origin of metabolic rhythms in cells (*19*).

As these simple living forms evolved into more complex organisms, the structure and function of photoreceptors concurrently increased in complexity. The flatworms (Planaria) possess retinulae capable of receiving only those light rays perpendicular to their broad surface (*10*). Some annelids, molluscs, and other advanced invertebrates have primitive concave retinas with minute apertures to focus the light. It is doubtful, however, that these simple systems can form detailed images. The octopus is exceptional in its advanced optic system and has been studied more intensively than other molluscs. Ultimately in phylogeny, higher mammals acquired light-focusing eyes and binocular vision. This yields an important generalization for further theory development, namely that photoreceptors increasingly elaborated during evolution to maximize the collection of divergent rays emanating from points in space.

Nervous system elaboration paralleled the development of photoreceptors. Protozoa contain no specialized nerve organelles with the possible exception of the silver-line system in ciliates (*20; 28*). The coelenterates contain simple nerve networks allowing some response differentiation but not producing fine behavioral coordination. Molluscs, arthropods, and birds acquired central nerve masses precedent to the massive cerebral tissue in higher mammals (*26; 5*). Elaboration and specialization of nerve tissue provided greater autonomy for the organism and allowed it to exploit the land environment by coordinating sensory reception with locomotion.

It is most interesting that nerve conduction, induced by light or by mechanical or chemical stimulation, is a periodic discharge whose frequency in many cases contains information about the intensity or quality of sensory stimulation (*15; 4*). Internalized periodic activity is therefore the major means whereby the organism receives information and transmits it to central nerve centers. In the nerve centers, selection and association mechanisms route the impulse to appropriate effector organs. The increase in mass of central nerve tissue and the elaboration of complex photoreceptors are both specializations of a fundamental organic function induced by periodic stimuli early in phylogeny.

Ontogenetic Parameters

During maturation, the human organism is repeatedly exposed to visual stimulation by the production of images on the retina. Through such repeated exposure to a succession of visual patterns and consequent cognition, the organism develops a perceptual set predisposing it to perceive spatially contiguous bodies as having common properties (*3*, pp. 13–18). To develop this concept of spatial perception more completely, a careful analysis of retinal images and their corresponding objects in space will be required.

In unobstructed space, light rays emanating from a point on an illuminated object spread out in all directions as rays passing through all points in the surrounding space. Theoretically, therefore, there are infinitely many positions in space at which the eye can receive an image of an object point. This capacity of the environment to emit multiple rays allows the viewer to obtain information about an object from many different perspectives. When a composite of such points, including all those in the visual field, is considered, the slight movement of the eye will cause the retinal image to change as new rays are admitted and previous rays excluded. If the shift in visual angle is slight, a great proportion of the image will remain partially unchanged. Thus there is repetition in changing visual patterns as a result of eye movement or locomotion of the body through space. Moreover, elements in the visual field which are closely proximate have a greater probability of remaining in the retinal image when the angle of viewing is shifted than elements widely separated.

During early development, repeated scanning movements of the eye produce a succession of overlapping retinal images, inducing a perceptual bias in the developing organism to anticipate repetition in sensory assimilation. Thus the ontogenetic origin of spatial perception is partly resident in the sequential series of retinal images in which each successive image has some properties in common with the preceding one. Moreover, spatially proximate bodies will always be associated in the retinal image for a time, whereas spatially distant objects will always be separated, as the eye scans the horizon. The constancy of association of proximate spatial bodies in successive retinal patterns further enhances the perceptual bias to perceive two spatially proximate bodies as having common properties.

Given such a perceptual bias, broadly generalized to include a wide range of stimuli, the organism will readily assimilate serially ordered stimuli when they contain common properties. Temporally contiguous responses which are repetitively aroused will become associated due to their homology to temporal relations of spatially related objects: two bodies in close spatial proximity produce images on the retina in close temporal proximity, whereas widely separated objects, depending on their distance from the viewer, produce successive images with long temporal delays between their formation. The organism, therefore, comes to perceive stimuli or responses occurring in close temporal succession as having common properties.

No doubt stimuli and responses occurring in close temporal succession also arouse common neural elements, thereby providing a physiological explanation for their psychological association. Molecular models of learning support this thesis. One paradigm (27) assumes that memory is the product of stored neuron-exciting molecules. The macromolecules formed during stimulation are stored in glial-like cells. The macromolecules consist of pools containing non-identical but overlapping distributions of the neuron-exciting molecules. Consequently recall is produced by the excitation of one cell in the series whose released molecules trigger in succession the remaining cells. These released molecules in turn excite neurons sequentially to produce the serial recall of prior experience.

The effects of repeated visual experiences during early postnatal ontogeny induce a perceptual set to perceive spatially proximate bodies as being related. Then, secondarily, temporally proximate stimuli are perceived as related. This association is induced by the close temporal formation of retinal images of spatially proximate bodies and also by the excitation of common neurons during the serial stimulation accompanying these experiences. The organism first becomes sensitive to spatial cues and their relationships before progressing to an awareness of temporal relations.

Ultimately the human organism becomes adept in symbolic relations as an extension of the prior learned relations of space and time. Indeed, the symbolic manipulations of man in their most effective forms (such as languages) consist of sequences of repetitive elements. The languages of man and the calls of lower animals are all characterized by periodic or repetitive patterns of sound wherein contiguous units contain some common elements. It is postulated that this periodicity is the product of natural selection by environmental periodic events during phylogeny and exposure to diverse repetitive stimuli during ontogeny.

Learning and Communication

Learning, then, is in part a function of response contiguity, a process whereby the repetitive arousal or the close temporal occurrence of responses in a sequence occasions associations among the responses. These associations are formed largely through the mediation of sensory and nerve organs acquired during phylogeny and stimulated during ontogeny to readily assimilate repetitive or temporally contiguous stimuli.

Effective communication, therefore, requires that contiguous statements contain some verbal elements in common. Coherent human language is an instance of this sort where successive statements in discourse contain a common idea. That is, the verbal content of one statement is integrated with that of the next statement in a communication sequence. Assuming that a perceptual bias exists to maximize reception of repetitive stimuli, such a coherent communication will be more effective than one containing statements with unrelated verbal content.

Reduced to its simplest state, maximum communication effectiveness occurs when the same statement is reiterated, producing a "stamping in," or practice effect, in verbal learning. Although repetition of this sort is *effective* for communicating a limited amount of verbal content during brief periods of time, it is not *efficient* in maintaining pupil attention and communicating larger masses of content where new thoughts must be introduced as the communication unfolds. In other words, some repetition of verbal content increases communication effectiveness, whereas the inclusion of new verbal material at each step increases its efficiency. Extended sequences of communicated content will be both effective and efficient when contiguous verbal utterances (statements) contain some content in common but also include new content as the communication sequence unfolds.

A Concept of Classroom Communication Structure

Based on this theory, a concept of structure in teaching, called *kinetic structure,* has been formulated in terms of the serial organization of a communication and the relatedness (through attributes held in common) of contiguous communicated statements. Temporal contiguity of two verbal stimuli is sufficient to induce an association between their complementary responses. Contiguity alone, however, may account for only a small portion of the maximum strength of the association. When evoked in such a way that they hold attributes or elements in common, contiguous responses will have greater association strength. The role of contiguity and common properties in serially communicated knowledge has been explained in *Structure in Teaching* (3, pp. 18–22). It may be consulted for additional details concerning theoretical principles underlying the discussion presented in this book.

Some special terms will be used in describing communication. A *discourse unit* is a verbal statement defined conceptually as a single utterance equivalent to a complete grammatical thought. Classroom discourse, of course, often includes both teacher statements (*stimulus units*) and student responses. In the present investigation, the discourse units to be analyzed are stimulus units; and when contiguous discourse units are referred to, this will mean successive teacher statements even when there are in fact intervening student response units. The *verbal elements* of a discourse unit are the words or phrases (or symbols representing these) considered substantive or essential to the unit. Operational definitions for the identification of discourse units and verbal elements are given in Chapter II. *Commonality,* which will be used frequently, means the condition of holding elements in common. Commonality in *unit pairs* (pairs of contiguous discourse units) means that contiguous units contain some elements in common.

Commonality and Contiguity

We will be using the concepts of commonality and contiguity to explain the strength and serial association of responses. In operational terms, the *strength* of a response is its persistence as measured by the probability of its being aroused by a given stimulus; and the *serial association* of responses is the arousal of a series of responses in a given order when the first response is supplied as a stimulus.

A principle relating these aspects of knowledge acquisition to commonality and contiguity is stated as follows: *Enhanced serial association and strength of verbal responses will occur when contiguous responses hold elements in common.*

Since verbal responses are often acquired through verbal stimuli, there is a complementary principle for the organization of verbal communications: *Acquisition of verbal responses will be enhanced when they are evoked by a communication wherein contiguous stimulus units hold elements in common.*

In summary, these two principles taken together state that the strength and serial association of responses aroused by a communication are directly related to the commonality among discourse units in the communication.

Since commonality is a central concept in acquisition of knowledge, we shall be giving close attention to quantitative methods for assessing it. Commonality among discourse units will be measured by counting the number of verbal elements held in common by pairs of discourse units. Commonality, therefore, is the central concept whereby we identify the presence of structure in a communication. Commonality is achieved when any one or more of the verbal elements in a discourse unit are identical to those in a contiguous unit. Maximum commonality occurs when the verbal elements are *all* identical, thereby producing essential repetition of a unit. Extended use of repetition depresses assimilation of a communication; and for reasons explained later, other forms of periodicity may be employed to circumvent excessive repetition and its deleterious effects. Some commonality in contiguous discourse units enhances their communication value. This principle is embodied in the definition of kinetic structure as serial-order relatedness among discourse units in a communication.

The *degree of kinetic structure* in a communication is the extent to which contiguous discourse units contain elements in common. In other words, it is the *amount* of contiguity and commonality among discourse units. To assess the degree of kinetic structure, one must first specify what elements or properties of discourse units are to be examined. In some cases, the common elements will be verbal elements, certain specified words appearing in the discourse units. They may also be spatial or temporal properties denoted by words. When a communication contains a set of words which appear repeatedly in such a way as to link together the discourse units, kinetic structure will be high. The degree of structure will correspond to the number of matching words in pairs of discourse units. Thus, there may be themes which extend throughout a communication sequence, giving it commonality and hence structure.

Organizational Dimensions

The kind of kinetic structure based on distributional relations among the word elements of contiguous discourse units is said to be based on a "derived" organizational dimension. A *dimension* is a mode of serial organization. A *derived dimension* is a sequence wherein commonality is achieved through the repetition of words or other symbols without necessarily specifying their intentional meanings. However, when a series of linking elements refer specifically to spatial attributes—the position and orientation of objects in space—the underlying organizational mode is a *spatial dimension.* A spatial dimension, when used as a criterion sequence or plan for a communication, contains a list of all the objects to be described in a serial order identical to their order of occurrence in the actual system.

The following list is a spatial dimension containing selected components of the circulatory system. The heart is chosen as the first component and the remaining ones are arranged in order of increasing distance from the heart:

1. The heart and its composite vessels
2. Pulmonary veins and arteries
3. Systemic veins and arteries

A communication sequence presented in the above manner would have a high degree of kinetic structure with reference to spatial relatedness of the communicated items. Commonality is produced by the representation of common spatial properties in contiguous discourse units. Temporal attributes may also be used to achieve a high degree of kinetic structure, by listing events in the same order as that of their natural or imagined occurrence. Commonality in such a *chronological dimension* is achieved through shared temporal properties being described in each pair of contiguous discourse units.

Three brief examples of classroom discourse will be presented here to illustrate discourse organized with reference to (1) a spatial dimension, (2) a chronological dimension, and (3) a derived dimension.

(1) A *spatial dimension* is illustrated in a lesson on avian skeletal anatomy. There are eleven discourse units, presenting an anterior-to-posterior spatial description of the breastbones in a bird. Since the sequence is clearly organized with reference to the spatial position and orientation of the bones, it is spatially organized.

1. Now the furcula is really the uniting of the two collar bones or clavicles, right here in the front, to form what is known as this furcula.
2. It's this entire V-shaped process here which is called the furcula. OK?
3. And the major importance or significance of this furcula is that it serves for attachment of this very heavy flight muscle, all right?
4. Now there is one more structure here which is most peculiar to the bird and these are these bones here.
5. Can you see these here, just in back or posterior to the furcula?
6. Now these are called coracoid bones.
7. And again these occur in birds.
8. They are supportive structures.
9. And how they support it is that they support the furcula to the shoulder process. OK?
10. Well, it braces or supports the shoulder bones to the furcula and also to the sternum or breastbone itself. All right?
11. Now these as far as the pectoral girdle are concerned are the only features that are distinctive to the bird group.

(2) A *chronological dimension* is exhibited in a lesson on the circulatory system. Notice how the temporal order of events in the flow of blood is presented in a sequence proceeding from a central to a peripheral zone in a mammalian body, corresponding to a basic spatial dimension for the circulatory system as presented on page 9. There are nine numbered discourse units and four unnumbered student responses (preceded by four short dashes).

1. We have just a minute or two to go on now and look at the anatomy, the anatomy of the circulatory system.
2. What does anatomy mean?

---- It means like opening up, looking at, observing structures.

3. Right, it's the structure of the circulatory system.

4. And there are several different structures here which can be mentioned.
5. First of all, the heart itself.
6. Where does the blood go when it leaves the heart?

---- To all parts of the body.

7. What does it go through?

---- Uh, the arteries.

8. Arteries, right. After going through arteries, what are the names of the next little vessels that it goes through?

---- Uh, capillaries?

9. Capillaries, OK.

(3) A *derived dimension* is taken from the same lesson as the chronological dimension. In this brief communication, the word *cell* and its associated terms link the discourse units together and confer commonality.

1. There are three different things that we can point out as being the main components of the blood.
2. Two of these are cells.
3. And one of them is more a liquid kind of material.
4. What's the name of one of the kinds of cells?

---- Oh, white cells, corpuscles.

5. All right, white blood cells or what?

---- Corpuscles.

6. All right, corpuscles; corpuscles is another word you can use instead of cell.
7. So we have cells called white cells or white corpuscles.
8. What's another kind of cell that we find in the blood?

---- Red, uh, cells.

9. All right, red cells or again red corpuscles if you want to call them that.

In this third communication, there is no clear reference to spatial or chronological properties; the discourse units are related to one another largely through a description of various cells. The identification of the sequence as a derived dimension can be determined objectively by simply counting the number of times the word *cell* appears in proportion to all other substantive words.

Either a matching elements method or a serial comparison

method can be used to assess degree of kinetic structure with reference to derived dimensions, in terms of verbal commonality, as will be explained in Chapter II. The serial comparison method as developed thus far produces only one coefficient of structure, whereas the matching elements method, including the use of Kinetograms, is much more powerful in elucidating organizational patterns in communications. It is the matching elements method, with its rich yield of information, to which attention is primarily devoted in this book.

A serial comparison method for assessing degree of kinetic structure as determined by a spatial or chronological dimension is described in *Structure in Teaching* (pages 24–25, 30–31, and Appendix A).

Organizational dimensions can be arranged in a hierarchy based on their complexity and abstraction. The order of increasing abstraction is: spatial, chronological, derived. In addition to their role as a context for the organization of communications, dimensions are also analogs of stages in human cognitive growth. Spatial representations are the first to be acquired in ontogeny. These are followed in course by temporal representations and ultimately in later childhood by verbal or symbolic cognitive forms. The organization of communications may also be hierarchical. Spatial and temporal sequences may be nested within longer sequences organized in accordance with symbolic or derived dimensions. Thus, the genetic hierarchy of cognitive organizational patterns is sometimes recapitulated in the nested patterns of verbal organizational dimensions. The hierarchical organization of nested dimensions is illustrated in the following example.

I may describe the operation of a clock at several levels of abstraction. First, the spatial arrangement of the various components; then, their meshing and interaction during the process of regulating the movement of the hands; and finally, both of these as related to the meaning of the concept of time. The latter concept integrates the whole communication and provides symbolic commonality among its discourse units. The ontogenetic order of cognitive development—namely, spatial, chronological, and abstract-symbolic—is recapitulated in such a communication.

Of course, there are other ways of organizing this same material, and the nested hierarchy is only one example frequently encountered in natural science lessons. Empirical studies by Piaget and other developmental psychologists have clearly established the hierarchical development of cognition as it proceeds through spatial, chronological, and formal–symbolic stages. Olson and

Baker (*23*) found that young children (mean age 4 years, 4 months) who had not yet acquired verbal comprehension of spatial directions could nevertheless cognitively represent changes in position of objects, as evidenced by their operations upon the objects while blindfolded. Olson and Baker cite evidence pointing toward spatial representations of the environment as fundamental cognitive processes subserving higher-order formal operations. DeSoto, London, and Handel (*13*) have shown that human reasoning about nonspatial orderings is accomplished through spatial representations of the relations among the ordered items. Their subjects were college undergraduates. Bruner (*8*) has given a very interesting account of the course of cognitive development in his paper on this subject.

Verbal Dimensions of Kinetic Structure Analysis

Some additional properties and theoretical issues pertinent to *derived dimensions* will be presented here as a foundation for the methodologies to be presented in Chapter II.

Commonality

A derived dimension is organized on the principle that contiguous discourse units of a given communication sequence will have the maximum possible number of verbal elements in common, or, alternatively, that some periodic pattern of organization is employed to partially spare this requirement. When verbal communications have a high degree of kinetic structure based on a derived dimension, contiguous discourse units will hold a large proportion of their verbal elements in common.

Indeed, the *fundamental coefficient* of kinetic structure derived for this investigation (B_1), using a matching elements method and based on a derived dimension, is a quantitative expression of the degree of verbal commonality in pairs of discourse units. For each unit pair,

$$B_1 = \frac{n_1}{n_0 + n_1},$$

where n_1 is the number of matched elements and n_0 is the number of unmatched elements in the pair. (The elements counted are, of course, only those considered substantive or essential to the content, which are coded as explained in Chapter II.) An alternative kinetic structure coefficient B_2, also a measure of commonality but weighted to reflect the saliency of unmatched elements, will be defined later (page 34).

Maximum structure occurs when B_1 equals 1.0. In this condition commonality is maximum, meaning that the coded elements in contiguous discourse units are identical. Minimum kinetic structure occurs when B_1 equals 0, which means that the units contain no coded elements in common; there is no commonality. The receiver of the communication may, however, supply linking elements, thereby expending energy to supply commonality among otherwise discrete discourse units.

Theoretically, the ease of acquisition and stability of acquired associations will be directly related to the degree of kinetic structure in a communication. When kinetic structure is maximum and B_1 equals 1.0, there is obviously repetition or "stamping in" of essentially identical discourse units. The limited knowledge presented thus repetitively would theoretically increment in strength with each repetition if fatigue and cognitive saturation effects were neglected.

However, extended maximum structure does not in fact achieve maximum response strength, because the pupil will shift attention and no longer perceive excessively repetitious material; moreover, little progress in adding new increments of knowledge will be attained. There is no progress toward adding new verbal elements when a stamping-in procedure is employed. Therefore, to maintain pupil attention and to progress into new material, the kinetic structure of a communication should, on the average, be less than maximum. That is, $\bar{B}_1 < 1.0$. Under these conditions fatigue will be reduced and some progression achieved. A more detailed discussion on the reasonable values of $\bar{B}_1$ to expect in a communication will be presented following discussion of progression.

Progression

Progression (P) is defined as the rate of inclusion of unmatched verbal elements in a series of discourse units. For a given unit pair, its quantitative measure is

$$P = 1 - B_1,$$

where B_1 is the fundamental coefficient of structure. Thus P is the ratio of the number of unmatched coded elements (n_0) to all coded elements ($n_0 + n_1$) in a pair of discourse units, unmatched elements being new elements relative to a unit pair. (A variable called "progression density" will be defined later in terms of new elements in a total span.)

A quantitative estimate of progression can also be made by computing the mean number of unmatched verbal elements in a specified sequence of discourse units. This coefficient (p) is the number of unmatched verbal elements in N discourse units divided by N. In all analyses to be reported later, the coefficient of progression, P, will be used.

When P is computed for a span of S discourse units, we obtain the following formula for *total progression* in that span.

$$P_S = \sum_{i=s}^{s'} (1 - B_1)_i.$$

The limits s and s' refer respectively to the first and last discourse unit number in a span of S units.

Progression Intensity

Progression intensity (I) will be defined as the cognitive potency of newly introduced verbal elements. Whereas progression (P) concerns only the frequency of occurrence of unmatched verbal elements, progression intensity (I) pertains in addition to the potency of these elements.

Potency of verbal elements can be operationally assessed in at least two ways: (1) Ask the pupils who have previously received a communication to recall as many of the important verbal elements in the communication as they are able. The rank order of the words in their lists indicates the relative potency of each. Presumably, the most potent words would be listed first and the least potent last. (2) The analyst—or his computer—counts the total number of times each coded element appears in a communication. Potency is then determined on the basis that the more frequently a word appears, the more salient it will become to the receiver of a communication. Although this definition neglects the role of pupil biases in their selective attending to various words, it is a very reliable procedure. It deals with measurable attributes of the communication itself. Because of the objectivity of this method, it will be used in preference to the pupil questionnaire method.

Potency, then, will be defined as the relative frequency of occurrence of a coded verbal element when compared to the total frequency of all coded elements in a communication. The weighting factor

$$W = \left[\frac{F' + F''}{\Sigma f}\right]^{1/2},$$

used in calculating B_2 values, is the measure of potency. It is a relative frequency coefficient (explained on page 35) of the sort suggested in item 2 above.

Progression intensity (I) will be measured using B_2 units. For a pair of discourse units it is defined symbolically as

$$I = 1 - B_2.$$

Thus, since $1 - B_2 = PW$, the value of I is an estimate of the degree of unmatching of elements ($P = n_0/n_0 + n_1$) when modified by the potency (W) of the elements.

The total progression intensity I_S for a span S of discourse units is

$$I_S = \sum_{i=s}^{s'} (1 - B_2)_i.$$

The symbols s, s', and S are the same as those in the formula for the total progression coefficient P_S.

Both coefficients of progression, namely P_S and I_S, have dimensions expressed in units of area. The area is that contained within a histogram where each bar has height $1 - B_1$ or $1 - B_2$ and a base equal to unity representing one discourse unit. When all of the bars are summed for a span S, the total area is that contained within the histogram for P_S or I_S respectively. A progression intensity (I_S) histogram, moreover, contains an area analogous to that bounded within the lines of a Kinetogram, which is a graph of B_2 structure coefficients. It represents an estimate of the area under the graph. In Figure 1, a Kinetogram segment and its corresponding progression intensity histogram are exhibited to demonstrate the analogous shaded areas bounded in the two graphs.

Progression intensity provides a measure of the potency of discontinuities in a series of discourse units. Progression intensity is

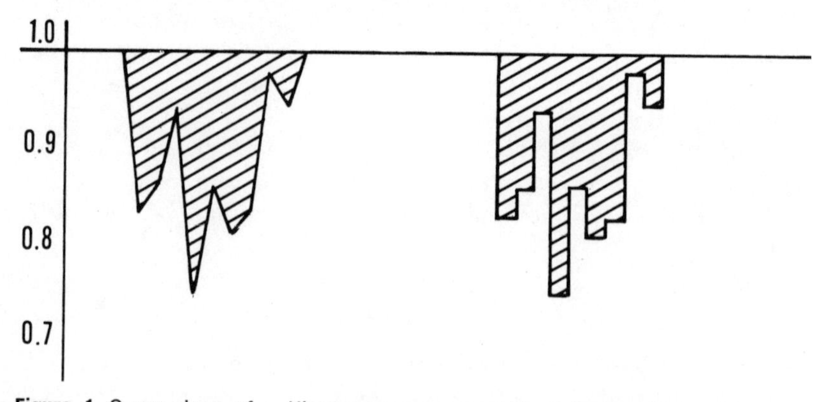

Figure 1. Comparison of a Kinetogram span and its corresponding progression intensity histogram.

also an estimate of the area bounded within a Kinetogram segment, the latter also being a visual cue to the amount of progression in the span. Progression (P_S) concerns only the number of unmatched elements in a span, whereas progression intensity (I_S) accounts for non-matching and the potency of the unmatched elements as well. Progression and progression intensity, when plotted as histograms on the same axis, are useful inventions in the analysis of segments of discourse called *gain series* and *decay series*. These will be discussed fully and illustrated in the chapter on methodology.

When discourse spans are being compared for progression (P_S) or progression intensity (I_S), the mean values must be used. The formula for mean progression in a span containing S discourse units is of course P_S/S, or

$$\bar{P}_S = \frac{\sum_{i=s}^{s'} (1 - B_1)_i}{S},$$

and mean progression intensity for a span of S discourse units is I_S/S, or

$$\bar{I}_S = \frac{\sum_{i=s}^{s'} (1 - B_2)_i}{S}.$$

Progression Density

In many cases a more meaningful comparison among spans of discourse can be made using the concept of *progression density*—the extent to which *new* unmatched verbal elements are introduced in a span (sequence) of discourse units (*new* elements being those appearing for the first time *in the span*, whether or not they appear in prior spans).

The progression density of a unit pair is defined only relative to a given span:

$$D = (1 - B_1) \cdot n,$$

where n is the number of elements *new to the span* in the *second unit* of the pair. This coefficient is thus a product with a density factor n and a progression factor $P = 1 - B_1$.

The total progression density for a span is the sum of these products, the products being computed in the order of their occurrence, beginning with the first:

$$D_S = \sum_{i=s}^{s'} [(1 - B_1)_i \cdot n_i].$$

To compute the product D for each successive unit pair, then, one finds $1 - B_1$ for the pair and multiplies this by the number of new verbal elements in the second unit of the pair. The first unit of a span is considered to have $n = 0$, so its $1 - B_1$ value need not be known.

The following array representing a span of discourse units will illustrate the method. The element code numbers are shown for each unit, with the italicized codes representing the new elements. Also shown are the values of B_1, $1 - B_1$, and n at each unit, and the products $D = (1 - B_1) \cdot n$. The coefficient of progression density D_S for this span is the sum of the products in the last column: $D_S = 5.21$.

Discourse Unit Number	*Verbal Element Codes*	B_1	$1 - B_1$	n	$(1 - B_1)n$
1	1, 2, 3	–	–	0	.00
2	3, *4*	0.40	.60	1	.60
3	3, *5*, 2	0.40	.60	1	.60
4	3, 4, *6*	0.33	.67	1	.67
5	6, *7*, *8*	0.33	.67	2	1.34
6	6, 8	0.80	.20	0	.00
7	*9*, *10*, 2	0.00	1.00	2	2.00
8	9, 4, 3	0.33	.67	0	.00

When comparing different spans of discourse, the *mean* progression density ($\bar{D}_S$) must be used. For a given span this is computed by dividing total progression density D_S by the number of units in the span:

$$\bar{D}_S = \frac{\sum_{i=s}^{s'} [(1 - B_1)_i \cdot n_i]}{S}.$$

For the span of eight units represented above, $\bar{D}_S = 5.21/8 = 0.65$.

Mean progression density is often reported in combination with another coefficient called the *new activity coefficient:*

$$NAC = \frac{\sum_{i=s}^{s'} n_i}{S},$$

the average number of new elements per unit in a given span. For the span above, $NAC = 7/8 = 0.88$, meaning that in this span new elements are introduced, on the average, at the rate of a little less than one per unit. *NAC* is often reported as a parenthetical quantity following $\bar{D}_S$ (but not to be taken as a multiplier). Thus, for the example above we would enter, in a tabulation of $\bar{D}_S$ values, 0.65 (0.88).

Clearly, the mean progression density coefficient ($\bar{D}_S$) is more informative and comprehensive than the mean progression coefficient ($\bar{P}_S$). *Mean progression density, together with the new activity coefficient, should always be used in making comparisons among discourse spans with reference to the progressive elaboration of verbal content in the spans.* The higher the $\bar{D}_S$ and *NAC* values, the greater the amount of progressive elaboration.

Progression and Commonality in Verbal Learning

Progression and commonality vary inversely with one another. When commonality is maximum ($B_1 = 1$), progression is minimal ($1 - B_1 = 0$). When progression is maximum ($1 - B_1 = 1$), commonality is minimal ($B_1 = 0$), since there are no matching elements. Too much progression can be deleterious to acquisition, since there will be few properties in common among contiguous units and pupils will either fail to associate the units in a series or expend so much work supplying linking associations that acquisition will be depressed. In an efficient communication, there must be a reasonable balance between commonality and progression. New ideas should continually appear (progression), but they should also be related to preceding ideas (commonality). Some progression density is necessary not only to provide accretion of new verbal material but also as an arousal factor to counteract saturation and fatigue engendered by much repetition.

Progression also has the significant function of differentiating responses in a series. In teaching, we often relate two bits of knowledge and then give them perceptual saliency by citing the contrasts or unmatching attributes as well. Each time responses are so differentiated, progression is used, since unmatching or "different" attributes must be introduced. Such response differentiation, as a function of controlled progression, engenders saliency for those responses by giving them unique attributes. The responses, moreover, having been previously related to prior learned responses, also gain stability through association in a series. Hence, this practical example illustrates the efficacy of a reasonable balance between commonality (similarities) and progression (unique attributes) as employed in the practice of teaching.

From these examples, we might expect that the mean fundamental coefficients $\bar{B}_1$ for most lessons would occur in a range near 0.50. In fact, all of the lessons analyzed thus far by these methods have $\bar{B}_1$ values falling within the range of 0.28 to 0.44, apparently depending on the kind of lesson. Further analyses of $\bar{B}_1$ values are presented in Chapter III.

When there is an equal balance between commonality and progression, then $\bar{B}_1 = 0.50$. In this case, the number of new verbal elements introduced in successive discourse units of a communication would be equal on the average to the number of elements held in common within the pairs. Analyses using the mean fundamental coefficient $\bar{B}_1$ in combination with B_2 values plotted as a Kinetogram will allow much more thorough examinations of the relationship of commonality to progression in a communication.

Each pupil will undoubtedly be unique in his requirement for some particular balance between progression and commonality to attain maximum acquisition. Future research on such balance requirements as a function of intelligence, anxiety, creativity, and so forth will yield principles whereby greater precision can be achieved in matching lesson structure to the unique needs of the pupils.

Theoretically, there are several ways of achieving a reasonable balance between progression and commonality other than massively reducing one to enhance the other.

Cascaded Chains

One alternative scheme is to use a *cascaded chain* organization (*1*). As a basis for discussion of this mechanism, we must explore the attributes of a pauci-sequential communication. A communication is *pauci-sequential* when each topic is presented exclusive of all other topics—when there is little or no interspersion or mixing of topics. Thus, each set of verbal elements related to one topic is presented as a pure series independently of all other verbal elements. A pauci-sequential communication achieves high levels of commonality through close grouping of discourse units containing verbal elements in common.

The following illustration will clarify the concept. Suppose I plan to teach a lesson on cell division presenting the various phases of mitosis: interphase, prophase, metaphase, anaphase, telophase. Introductory statements describing each phase will be symbolized by capital letters: I, P, M, A, T. Statements of specific facts relevant to each phase will be symbolized by corresponding lower-case letters: i, p, m, a, t. An introductory statement for the interphase (I) as presented in a lesson might be as follows:

> The interphase is a period of time when the cell is metabolically active but not actively dividing.

This might be a specific factual statement (i) about the interphase:

> The nuclear membrane is clearly intact during the interphase and encloses the granular nucleoplasm.

A pauci-sequential arrangement of statements is symbolized as follows:

I–I–i–i–i–P–P–p–p–p–M–M–m–m–m · · ·

Progression can be increased, with minimal loss in commonality, by cascading the sequence, thus:

I–i–P–p–M–m–A–a–T–t–I–i–i–i–P–p–p–p · · ·

Here there is first a series of introductory statements giving an overview of all phases in their chronological order of occurrence, with very little specific elaboration of each. These are reiterated subsequently with greater elaboration of specifics. Strength of responses so acquired is enhanced through the periodic repetition of introductory statements with each statement subsuming a limited set of specifics. Commonality is conserved while progression is enhanced, thus increasing pupil arousal. Less cognitive fatigue and saturation are induced by a cascaded sequence than by a corresponding pauci-sequential communication.

Static Structure

Another mechanism for enhancing progression and reducing repetition is that of *static structuring*. Considerable loss in commonality may occur during static structuring. In this organizational mode, diverse topics are presented in contiguous discourse units. The associations among these units are usually multi-relational, having many responses associated with one another. Static-structured sequences, in comparison to high-kinetic-structured ones, may have lower commonality. Since commonality is reduced in a static-structured sequence, kinetic structure is also reduced. The high level of progression and the depressed level of commonality concurrent with static structuring reduce the efficiency of acquisition. There is sufficient dissimilarity among discourse units to cause a depression of encoding which requires the pupil to supply some linking elements, whereas these are already supplied in a high-kinetic-structured communication.

A Kinetogram is useful as a tool in analyzing a communication for static structure. Static structure appears as a series of spikes whose mean B_2 value is clearly lower than the mean B_2 value of the surrounding series of spikes. This means that the packet of spikes corresponding to a static-structured sequence is clearly depressed below the abscissa, and the upward directed peaks in the series do not rise as close to the abscissa as do surrounding peaks. The lower the mean value ($\bar{B}_2$) for a given span, the greater the amount of static structuring.

Communications containing static structures often contain classifying, evaluative, or analytical statements, where several diverse items are related. Although static structuring depresses the rate of knowledge acquisition, it may enhance subsequent divergent or creative use of the acquired knowledge. The possible salient effect of static structuring in enhancing creativity is in the increased probability that a response will be aroused by diverse cues. A necessary condition for divergent thinking is plasticity of behavior. Static structuring should enhance the probability that responses with multiple interrelations will be acquired, thus increasing the probability that any one response can be aroused by diverse stimuli. A stimulus arousing any one of the many responses with which a particular response is associated will also arouse that response, through indirect association. Hence, the more multiple connections a response has, the more likely it is to be aroused; thus such connections contribute to divergent or creative behavior. Static structuring is less likely to produce compulsive use of knowledge than high kinetic structure.

Two sequences of discourse will be shown here to illustrate (1) high-kinetic-structured and (2) high-static-structured discourse. The mean weighted coefficients $\bar{B}_2$ for these sequences are respectively 0.91 and 0.77.

The following sequence has high kinetic structure.

1. All right, behavior is inherited—behavior in birds.
2. And I have an article that has to do with the inheritance of behavior in lovebirds.
3. All right, did you know that there was such a thing as a lovebird, a real one?
4. They're parrots, or related to the parrots, in the picture of different species of lovebirds.
5. You can see that they look a lot like parrots.
6. Now they can trace the evolution of the lovebirds on the basis of their behavior.
7. All right, down here—these are the primitive forms, the first ones in the evolution.

8. And then it goes up, till these were the intermediate.
9. These are called the peach-faced lovebirds.

A static-structured communication, composed of some multi-relational statements and contrasts, is shown here:

1. Remember, I said that in the process of forming the sex cell, you'll break this down into three?
2. Well, the mistake for mongolism occurred in this division.

---- If they're not split right . . . mutation?

3. Yeah, except that this mutation won't be passed on to the next generation.
4. If you have any mistakes taking place here, it's not going to affect the next generation.

---- DNA?

5. Yeah, all of the chromosomes are DNA.
6. It's not in a sex cell.
7. These are like skin cells or hair cells, cells that make up your organs or the blood.
8. They're not going to be passed on to your offspring.
9. The only mistakes that are passed on are when they happen when you're forming the sex cell.

---- Do you mean only things that you are born with?

10. No, see there could be changes in you once you are born.
11. You can have mutations there.

The Kinetogram spans corresponding to these segments of discourse are shown in Figure 2. The mean weighted coefficient $\bar{B}_2$ alone is not sufficient to identify static-structured sequences. The form of the spikes in the Kinetogram must also be taken into account.

Acquisition of New Knowledge

Another matter relevant to balance between commonality and progression in a communication is the means whereby new knowledge becomes associated with already existing bodies of knowledge. Thus far, we have considered only the question of how new knowledge is acquired with facility and how strength, stability, and multiple associations among immediately acquired responses are related to the structure of a communication. The principles of contiguity and commonality will be used to explain connections between newly acquired responses and prior learned responses.

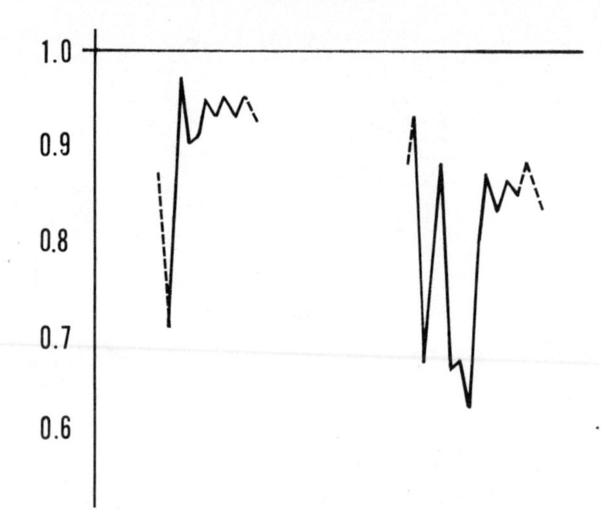

Figure 2. Comparison of high kinetic structure (left) and high static structure (right) as represented by Kinetogram spans. Each sequence begins with a large-amplitude spike, which is a sign that new verbal elements have been introduced at that point. Note the persistence of large-amplitude spikes and depressed peaks in the static-structure span.

When a new series of responses is to be related to existing ones, this can be achieved in part through temporal contiguity. Prior acquired responses are aroused, through questioning for example, and the new series is connected to them by immediately presenting it in contiguity. A stronger association will be facilitated when the new responses are connected to the existing series by citing verbal elements held in common between the two. By this means, the prior acquired response series is extended through association with a new series.

In another process of associating new responses with existing ones, commonality is produced by rephrasing the same material in many different ways. This procedure maximizes the probability that new knowledge will be associated meaningfully, through commonality, to knowledge acquired earlier. The rephrasing process eventually provides a context wherein some elements are identical to those in the pupil's existing body of knowledge. When this occurs—when the new material has elements in common with prior learned responses—association occurs spontaneously and the student usually signals the association by an enlightened facial expression which the teacher interprets as a cue that the pupil has finally comprehended.

A quasi-discovery lesson can sometimes be explained on the basis of commonality. The teacher organizes a lesson in segments, with few explicit allusions to common elements among the discrete segments. Finally, at the end of the communication, the teacher presents a statement, or questions the pupils until they produce a statement, wherein all the preceding discourse is interrelated. By this massive thrust of common elements at the end of a communication, the prior acquired knowledge is suddenly sequestered through commonality and the pupil experiences a contrived sense of insight or discovery. Of course, the lesson has to be carefully planned to ensure that the final presentation will subsume and integrate the prior presentations in the lesson.

Transitions

Commonality and contiguity may also be used to ensure a smooth or continuous transition between two contiguous major topics in a communication. With reference to the phenomenon of transitions, the degree of kinetic structure is determined (as explained in Chapter II) by the number of matching elements in contiguous parts of the transition sequence. When commonality and contiguity are thus used to produce a continuous transition between two major topics, the two segments are said to be *coupled,* and the transition is effected by a *coupling* or *coupler* (C). Such major topics are usually presented in extended sequences of discourse units, called "long units" in *Structure in Teaching* (3). (In this book, long units will be called "primary spans." Shorter units contained within primary spans or standing alone will be called "secondary spans.") If no commonality exists between spans, and they are not interrelated by methods of "mixing" as explained later, the transition is *non-coupled* (NC).

Examples of transitions in communication will be given here in two ways: (1) in symbolic models; and (2) in verbal sequences simulating discourse in teaching. All of the examples will contain or represent the same content as a means of pointing up their significant structural differences. In the symbolic models, alphabet letters will be used to represent discourse units containing references to given topics. Thus, A or B will represent a discourse unit referring exclusively to topic A or B respectively. When a discourse unit contains references to both topics, it will appear as –A,B–. As will be seen in the verbal models, the two topics are (A) the role of cellulose in plant physiology, and (B) the role of starch. In each verbal model, only the transitional portion of the sequence illustrated by the symbolic model will be presented. All the statements are simulated discourse units as they might be presented by a teacher.

Four types of transitions are identified: non-coupled transitions (NC); loose couplers (C-1); close couplers (C-2); mixed-mode couplers (C-3).

The *non-coupled transition* (NC) has no integration of topics between or within discourse units:

A—A—A—A—B—B—B—B

Only temporal contiguity of units containing A and B produces an association between the two topics. A verbal model follows:

1. OK, the cell wall contains a large proportion of cellulose. (A)
2. This substance gives rigidity and strength to the wall. (A)
3. Now I want to talk about starch, which should be of interest to you since it is our main source of food energy supplied by plants. (B)
4. Starch appears in the plant cell as a tiny grain with concentric layers. (B)

The three kinds of *coupled* transitions are discussed in ascending order of increasing strength.

In the *loose coupler* (C-1), no direct relationship is presented between two topics in a transition; there is no commonality among discourse units. However, a weak association is achieved by interspersing of topics, where each unit refers exclusively to one of the topics. Temporal contiguity and mixing effect an association:

A—A—A—*B*—A—B—B—B—B—B

There is some sacrifice of commonality when to produce contiguity two (or more) discourse units are intercalated. The two italicized units in the symbolic model above are intercalated. A verbal model follows.

1. OK, the cell wall contains a large proportion of cellulose. (A)
2. Starch is also a major carbohydrate in plant cells. (B)
3. Cellulose, however, imparts rigidity to the wall. (A)
4. Now we will discuss starch, which should be of interest to you since it is our main source of food energy supplied by plants. (B)

5. Starch appears in the plant cell as a tiny grain with concentric layers. (B)

In the *close coupler* (C-2), a direct relationship is stated or implied between verbal elements representing two different topics. The relationship is effected within a discourse unit. There may be only one or several of these statements in succession. There is no mixing or intercalation of statements referring to only one topic. Two C-2 couplers are symbolized as follows:

A—A—A—*A,B*—B—B—B

A—A—A—*A,B*—*A,B*—B—B—B

Maximum commonality is achieved in this kind of organization, where topics A and B are closely related in the transition. The italicized units in the array above are the close couplers. The following is a verbal example of a C-2 coupler:

1. OK, the cell wall contains a large proportion of cellulose. (A)
2. Cellulose gives rigidity to the plant cell wall. (A)
3. Now I would like to discuss starch with you, since it is a carbohydrate like cellulose. (A,B)
4. Starch should be of interest to you, since it is our main source of food energy from plants. (B)
5. Starch appears in plant cells as a tiny grain with concentric layers. (B)

Mixed-mode couplers (C-3) combine properties of C-1 and C-2 couplers. They are characterized both by mixing of discourse units and by close coupling. These are models of C-3 couplers:

A—A—A—B—A,B—A—B—B—B

A—A—A—B—A,B—A—A,B—B—B—B

There are several different possible combinations of mixed discourse units and close-coupled units in mixed-mode couplers. The ratio of the number of intercalated units to the number of close-coupled units gives a quantitative assay of the relative emphasis on contiguity as compared to commonality. A verbal model of a C-3 coupler follows:

1. OK, the cell wall contains a large proportion of cellulose. (A)
2. Starch also forms a large proportion of the carbohydrates in plant cells. (B)

3. In fact, you might say that starch and cellulose are the two major groups of carbohydrates in plants because of their abundance and physiological importance. (A,B)
4. Cellulose has the function of imparting rigidity to the cell wall. (A)
5. Starch should be of interest to you, since it is our main source of food energy when we eat plants. (B)
6. Starch appears in plant cells as tiny grains with concentric layers. (B)

Quantitative methods for the identification of these coupling modes and for the fine structural analysis of other limited spans of discourse will be presented in Chapter II.

CHAPTER II

Methods

Transcribing and Coding Audio-Records

Operational definitions of discourse units and coded verbal elements have been devised to help ensure standard and reproducible analyses.

Identifying Discourse Units

Discourse unit length and content will of course affect the values of structural coefficients. Careful application of the defining rules at the outset of an analysis is mandatory if there is to be any meaning in comparing results obtained by different analysts. In our hands, these rules yield 95 per cent or greater agreement among independent transcribers in the identification of discourse units. Each rule will be stated and exemplified here. In the examples, the beginning of a new discourse unit is marked by a slash.

1. *The basic unit.* The basic unit of discourse is a single clause —that is, an utterance containing a subject and a predicate.

> Well, let's go on now to a system which is of importance to the bird and to all animals, the digestive system. / Now we've already mentioned the fact that it has this beak or bill. / Now the beak or bill serves many purposes to the bird. / It serves, for one thing, as a pair of hands would in food gathering. / All right, for one thing it acts as a hand and as a mouth.

2. *Incomplete utterances.* (*a*) A word, phrase, or other grammatically incomplete utterance is combined with the preceding

clause if it is uttered by the same speaker. (*b*) If an incomplete utterance is preceded by a statement of another speaker but followed by a statement of the same speaker, it is combined with the following statement. (*c*) When an incomplete utterance occurs between statements of other speakers, it is accepted as a single discourse unit.

In the first example to follow, the incomplete utterance (in italics) is assigned to the preceding complete statement to form a single discourse unit.

> But there are two regions to the stomach. *The Proventriculus and ventriculus.* / Now the anterior proventriculus is, as I said, not very different in structure from the crop.

In the next example, the incomplete statement is assigned to a succeeding statement because it follows an utterance (marked by dashes) of a different speaker.

> Gravel particles again serve to mechanically break down the food. / It's a grinding process. / ---- Wouldn't this be a disadvantage, that gravel, because wouldn't it be extra weight for the flyer? / *Yes, extra weight.* Well, not only that, it restricts him to certain environments.

3. *Clauses connected by conjunctions.* (*a*) Speakers tend to utter long series of clauses connected by *and* or *so*. When this occurs, the clauses are separated at the conjunction to form individual discourse units. An example is shown below. (*b*) If only two clauses are joined by an *and*, these can be combined as a single discourse unit when the meaning of the statement is thereby enhanced or clarified. This option should be applied sparingly.

> Actually, if you were to look at it, you would have here a short esophagus, / and in this region you get a sort of outcropping or bulging of the digestive tract into a structure which you have met before, called a crop, / and again, as in the earthworm, this crop is very thin-walled.

4. *Conditional statements. If–then* statements are never separated into two discourse units. For example:

> If a species feeds particularly on insects that you find in very narrow crevices, the tendency would be for them to have a very long, narrow, slender bill.

5. *Intercalated discourse.* A clause or verb phrase intercalated within a subsuming clause is retained within the subsuming statement as part of a single discourse unit. For example:

> Actually there are three ducts from the liver, the liver being this lobed structure, which empty into here.

6. *Clauses beginning with "because."* When preceded by another statement by the same speaker, clauses beginning with *because* are combined with the preceding statement unless a speaker tends to run many statements together. Then, as with conjunctions, the clauses are separated at the *because*. The following is an example of two clauses linked by *because*.

> Reptiles are cold-blooded, because they have a mixing of venous and arterial blood.

When unique situations arise beyond the scope of these rules, the intent of the first rule should be applied—that is, to render the communication into the smallest possible discourse units where each approximates a grammatically complete thought. In preparing the transcript, discourse units are single-spaced with a double space between units. Pupil statements are preceded by dashes to set them apart from teacher statements, the latter being numbered consecutively.

Identifying Verbal Elements

The verbal elements coded for discourse analysis may be single words or terms composed of two or more words. The analyst will compile a table of verbal elements selected from the transcript, listing and numbering them in consecutive order of appearance in the transcript. The number assigned to each verbal element is its code number. The following criteria are to be used in identifying verbal elements.

1. Any technical word or term appearing in a standard dictionary, encyclopedia, or handbook, or constituting part of the recognized terminology of the subject matter being communicated, is a verbal element.
2. Any word or term used as a synonym for one of the above elements is coded as equivalent to that element.
3. Any word occurring with high frequency, other than common words such as *will, is,* and the like, is selected as a verbal element even if it fails to meet the criteria stated in rules 1 and 2.
4. When a term contains two words, they are listed together and coded as a single verbal element, not as two elements. Any term containing two or more words denoting an object, class of objects, or event is listed as a single verbal element. For example, *red blood cell* is equivalent to *erythrocyte,* and both are coded as the same verbal element and assigned the same code number. Additional examples of multiple-word

elements are *skin cell, ear drum, cell membrane,* and *population growth.* In science lessons examined thus far, multiple-word verbal elements on the average accounted for 20 per cent of the total number of elements coded.

5. General adjectives are separated from the nouns they modify to form separate verbal elements. Hence *tawny fur* is separated into *two* verbal elements. Although *gold standard* would be used as a single verbal element, *gold vase* is separated.
6. Usually verbal elements are nouns, adjectives, and verbs (listed here in order of decreasing importance). In general, the analyst should be generous in his selection of verbal elements rather than parsimonious. Coding too few elements is more deleterious than overcoding. Very general words such as *push, skid, allow,* and so forth are not selected as verbal elements unless they are used in place of a technical term having the same meaning. Such instances appear only infrequently.

The mean number of coded verbal elements per discourse unit for science lessons examined thus far was 2.4. Some discourse units have had as many as 7 verbal elements. These values can be taken only as a general guide in selecting and coding lesson transcripts. A sample list of the verbal elements extracted from the transcript exhibited in Appendix A is also presented in Appendix A. After the analyst has gained some experience in coding, the list of verbal elements can be compiled as the coding proceeds, each new term being identified upon its appearance. This procedure should be adopted only after sufficient proficiency is attained in coding from a preformulated list of verbal elements.

Coding the Transcript

The transcript is coded as follows.

1. Each discourse unit is examined to determine the presence of verbal elements, and their appropriate code numbers are entered in the right-hand margin (see Appendix A).
2. Pronouns referring to noun elements in preceding discourse units are assigned the same code number as the elements they represent.
3. Each verbal element is coded only once for a given discourse unit, irrespective of the number of times it appears in the unit.
4. When a pronoun and noun taken together represent a two-word term, the pair is assigned the code number of the term.

For example, *their shell,* where *their* refers to *mollusc,* will be coded as if it were *mollusc shell.*

The effects of idiosyncratic coding errors on B_1 and B_2 coefficients of structure will be discussed later, in the section on *Method Stability and Reproducibility.*

Analysis by the Matching Elements Method

In computing coefficients of structure by the matching elements method, discourse units are examined in pairs, beginning with the first two units and proceeding in succession throughout the total length of the transcript. A computer program is available from the author to compute the two such coefficients to be presented here (B_1 and B_2) and to tabulate their distribution in the whole communication being analyzed.

The Fundamental Coefficient, B_1

The *fundamental coefficient* of structure (B_1), as explained in Chapter I, is a measure of commonality in pairs of contiguous discourse units. It is defined as the number of matched verbal elements in a unit pair divided by the total number of verbal elements in the pair.

$$B_1 = \frac{n_1}{n_0 + n_1},$$

where n_1 is the number of matched and n_0 the number of unmatched elements in a unit pair.

An excerpt from a transcript will be used here to illustrate the computation of B_1 values. The coded verbal elements in each discourse unit are italicized, and superscripts identify them by their code numbers, which also appear summarized at the right.

1.	All right, we'll go on now to talk about the *red blood cells*^{1}—the second part of the *blood*^{2} here—what they do.	1, 2
2.	We mentioned *hemoglobin*^{3}, *red blood cells*^{1} being to a large extent made up of this *protein*^{4}.	3, 1, 4
3.	*This material*^{3} enables the *red blood cells*^{1} to pick up *oxygen*^{5}.	3, 1, 5
4.	So the second *function*^{6} we can say is that *cells*^{7} carry *oxygen*^{5}.	6, 7, 5

In the first pair of discourse units (units 1 and 2), the only matched elements are represented by the two instances of code number 1 in the coding for the pair, indicating that the term *red blood cells* appears in both units. The number of matched elements n_1 is therefore 2. (Note that n_1 is always an even number.) The unmatched elements are represented by the three remaining numbers in the coding: 2, 3, 4. Therefore $n_0 = 3$ and $n_0 + n_1 = 5$. Thus B_1 for this pair is 2/5, or 0.40.

For the second unit pair (units 2 and 3), the verbal elements are represented by a total of six codes (3, 1, 4; 3, 1, 5), of which four (3, 1; 3, 1) are matched. Therefore $B_1 = 4/6$, or 0.67.

The *mean fundamental coefficient* ($\bar{B}_1$) for a lesson or any specified sequence of discourse units is a measure of the average commonality of contiguous units.

When computing the mean B_1 or B_2 coefficient for a total communication, the number of coefficients summed is the number of pairs of units: if there are N discourse units, there are $N - 1$ coefficients to be summed. The sum is then also divided by $N - 1$. (By convention, when plotting a Kinetogram, we assign $B_1 = 1.0$ for the first unit in order to produce $B_2 = 1.0$ as a starting point on the abscissa; but these coefficients are not used in computing mean values.) In computing mean B_1 or B_2 for spans within a lesson, however, the number of coefficients summed is S, the number of discourse units in the span; the coefficient computed at the first unit of the span (by matching with the last unit of the previous span) is included in the sum, which is then divided by S.

Tabulating the percentages of B_1 values occurring within 0.1 unit intervals is a convenient way of summarizing the distribution of B_1 values produced by analyzing a lesson. This method is discussed in Chapter III of *Structure in Teaching* and illustrated in Kinetogram summary tables shown in appendices of this volume.

Certain methods of studying the fundamental coefficient B_1 in combination with the weighted coefficient B_2 can yield evidence about the organization of transitions within a communication and within short spans of discourse. These methods will be described in detail following discussion of the weighted coefficient.

Kinetograms: The Weighted Coefficient, B_2

The *weighted coefficient*, B_2, is the coefficient used in plotting Kinetograms of communication structure. It is a modified coefficient of commonality containing both a matching elements factor and a weighting factor.

$$B_2 = 1 - \left[\frac{n_0}{n_0 + n_1} \cdot \left(\frac{F' + F''}{\Sigma f}\right)^{1/2}\right].$$

The potency factor $[(F' + F'')/\Sigma f]^{1/2}$ is an estimate of the saliency of unmatched elements in a pair of discourse units. The terms in this expression are frequency counts obtained from the analysis of the total lesson. F' and F'' are evaluated for a given unit pair by identifying, in the first and second unit respectively, the unmatched element which has the highest frequency of occurrence in the coding for the total discourse under analysis. (In other words, for each unit of a pair, F is always the total frequency of the highest-frequency unmatched element.) Frequency in general is symbolized as f, and Σf is the total frequency of *all* elements in the sequence.

As an illustration, consider the first pair of discourse units in the sample excerpt shown above in the discussion of B_1 values. In the first discourse unit, only verbal element number 2 is unmatched, therefore its frequency in the total discourse is F'; let us assume it is 12. In the second discourse unit elements 3 and 4 are unmatched; assume their total frequencies are 10 and 5 respectively. Since the rule states that the largest frequency is to be chosen for F values, F'' is 10 in this case. Now, the B_2 value for this example, where we assume $\Sigma f = 440$, is computed as follows:

$$B_2 = 1 - \left[\frac{3}{3+2} \cdot \left(\frac{12+10}{440}\right)^{1/2}\right].$$

Therefore, B_2 for this discourse unit pair is 0.87.

The *mean weighted coefficient* ($\bar{B}_2$) can be used to estimate the degree of kinetic structure in a lesson when the potency of its elements is included as a factor.

When B_2 values are plotted, they form a graph with the abscissa marked off in discourse units and the ordinate in B_2 units. This graph is called a *Kinetogram,* since it is a graph of kinetic structure. A Kinetogram is used for two purposes: (1) to summarize the structure of a communication; (2) to aid in the analysis of organizational patterns in a communication.

The Kinetogram contains several characteristic forms used in diagnosing the structure of a communication. They are called *pulses, gain series, decay series,* and *symmetries.* These will be discussed in the order named.

Pulses

A *pulse* is a downward directed spike containing three or more defining points. *Narrow pulses* contain only three points. *Broad pulses* contain more than three points. Figure 3 illustrates a narrow and a broad pulse.

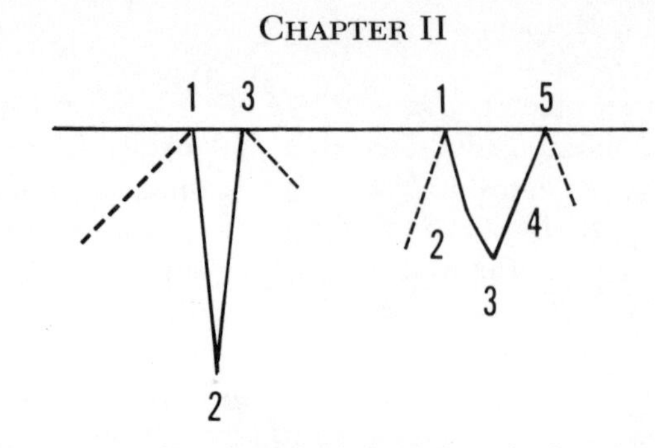

Figure 3. A narrow pulse (3 points) is shown left and a broad pulse (5 points) is shown right.

To prevent ambiguities in identifying the origins of pulses contained in a series, the second point is taken as the origin of the pulse. That is, the origin is that discourse unit coinciding with the first down point following the initial anchor point. This is reasonable from a theoretical standpoint, since the second point occurs when new verbal elements are introduced in the discourse, thus causing a fall in the curve at that point. The concluding point is the last one in the pulse, the final anchor point. Therefore, the corresponding span of discourse extends from the unit corresponding to the second point of the pulse through the unit corresponding to the final anchor point (in Figure 3, this is point 3 in the narrow pulse and point 5 in the broad pulse).

In describing pulses and other Kinetogram features, we will find it convenient to use somewhat elliptical language in referring to Kinetogram points and the B_1 and B_2 coefficients of the corresponding unit pairs in discourse. When we speak of the B_1 value of a point, for example, we mean the B_1 value computed for the unit pair whose second unit corresponds to that point (the point being actually the plot of the B_2 value of the given pair). By the B_1 or B_2 value of a discourse unit, we mean of course the value for the unit pair of which it is the second unit.

Both narrow and broad pulses can be subdivided into two classes: perfect and imperfect. A *perfect pulse* is one whose final anchor point lies on the abscissa; thus the B_1 value of the point is 1.0. An *imperfect pulse* is a spike whose final anchor point lies below the abscissa, with B_1 value less than unity. In a perfect pulse, the final discourse unit is one whose verbal elements are perfectly matched with those of the preceding unit. In an imperfect pulse, the final discourse unit contains potent unmatched elements which depress the final point below the abscissa.

Two forms of imperfect pulses are displayed in Figure 4. The necessary attributes are that the final anchor point (the one coinciding with a final peak) lies below the abscissa and has a B_1 value less than unity. As with perfect pulses, the beginning of the pulse is the second point, the one following the first anchor point. Anchor points are those coinciding with upward peaks.

Discourse consisting of a series of pulses in succession is called a *pulsed series,* since the information is presented in quanta or bursts. When a series contains perfect pulses, the quantized nature of the discourse is very obvious, since the last point of each perfect pulse corresponds to a discourse unit containing exactly the same verbal elements as the preceding one.

Imperfect pulses are subdivided into real and artificial pulses. A *real* imperfect pulse is one whose final anchor point is elevated as a result of commonality and not merely of reduced potency among unmatched elements. The B_1 value for the last anchor point will be greater than the preceding B_1 value when the imperfect pulse is real. This means that the final anchor point represents a discourse unit pair with increased relatedness, having more elements in common than the preceding unit pair. An *artificial* pulse occurs when the final anchor point is elevated merely because the unmatched elements in the unit pair are less potent than those in the preceding unit pair. An artificial gain in structure of this type occurs simply through the discontinuities in structure being less salient. The B_1 value for the final anchor point does not exceed that in the preceding point. The rise in the Kinetogram curve is explained by the increased B_2 value produced by the introduction of less potent (less frequently used) verbal elements in the final discourse unit. The degree of kinetic structure increases because of a decrease in the saliency of the unmatched verbal elements, rather than because of an increase in the number of matched verbal elements in the pair.

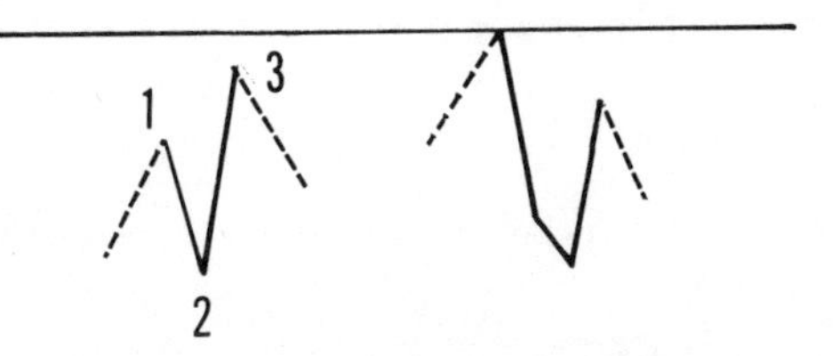

Figure 4. Two imperfect pulses are shown; the distinguishing characteristic is a depressed final anchor point.

Analysts must always remember that the B_2 value is a composite coefficient containing both a matching element factor (as a measure of commonality) and a weighting factor (as a measure of potency). When B_2 increases due to increased matching, the gain in kinetic structure is real. When an increase occurs because the unmatched elements are less potent than previously, the gain is artificial. The B_1 coefficient must be used in conjunction with the B_2 coefficient to determine whether gains are real or artificial. If a B_2 value increases while the corresponding B_1 value remains unchanged or decreases, the change in structure is artificial.

Series

A *gain series* is any span of points in a Kinetogram where the trend is upward. The B_2 values are increasing on the average in a gain series. Gain series can be either pulsed or linear. A *pulsed* gain series occurs when the upward trend of B_2 points is accompanied by a series of pulses as shown on the left in Figure 5. *Linear* gain series are composed of straight lines without pulses as shown on the right in Figure 5. In both cases, the trend of B_2 values for the total span is upward. A gain series, either pulsed or linear, is real if the B_1 values corresponding to B_2 values increase concomitantly. Artificial gain series are those in which B_1 values remain unchanged or decline.

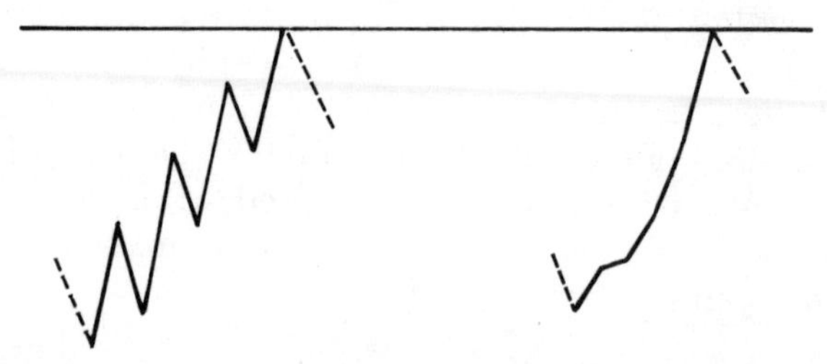

Figure 5. A pulsed gain series, shown left, contains an ascending array of spikes, whereas the linear gain series at the right is non-pulsed.

A *decay series* occurs where the Kinetogram undergoes a downward slope. There are *pulsed* and *linear* decay series, as illustrated in Figure 6. Decay series, like gain series, can be real or artificial.

The reality of gain or decay series can be assessed by simultaneously plotting progression (P) and progression intensity (I) histograms on the same base axis, as explained in Chapter I. Since

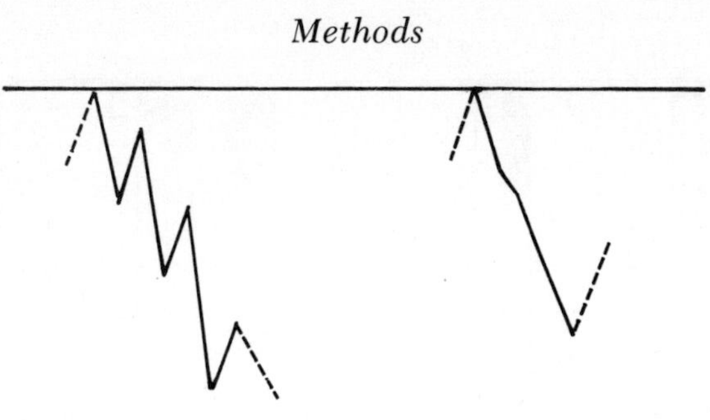

Figure 6. A pulsed decay series is shown on the left and a linear decay series at the right.

the progression coefficient for each point on the Kinetogram is $1 - B_1$ and the progression intensity is $1 - B_2$, these values when plotted simultaneously as a bar graph will provide visual evidence of variation between B_1 and B_2 coefficients.

If the overlapping histograms are similar—that is, if their bars vary more or less proportionately in height—then the gain or decay series is real. If not—that is, if the heights in one graph decrease or remain the same while those in the other increase—the series is artificial. A rapid estimate of reality or artificiality of a series can be made simply by examining the variation in B_1 and B_2 for the series. Usually if more than half of the B_1 and B_2 coefficients vary concomitantly, the series may be described as predominantly real.

Figure 7 contains eight composite progression histograms (simultaneous plots of progression and progression intensity), illustrating: real gain series, pulsed (*a*) and linear (*b*); artificial gain series, pulsed (*c*) and linear (*d*); real decay series, pulsed (*e*) and linear (*f*); artificial decay series, pulsed (*g*) and linear (*h*).

In some communications, Kinetogram gain or decay series are closely correlated in origin and conclusion with discourse topics. Thus, a particular theme as represented by a high frequency of one or several verbal elements may dominate a span of discourse units corresponding to a gain or decay series. In other communications, the speaker produces little correlation between gain or decay series and spans of particular discourse elements. This is a parameter which should be cited when performing analyses of structure. Thus, spans of gain series or decay series are reported as either correlated or non-correlated with specific activity of verbal elements.

The following examples A through H illustrate spans of discourse corresponding respectively to Figures 7*a* through 7*h*. These excerpts were in fact the source of the data used in plotting the graphs of Figure 7.

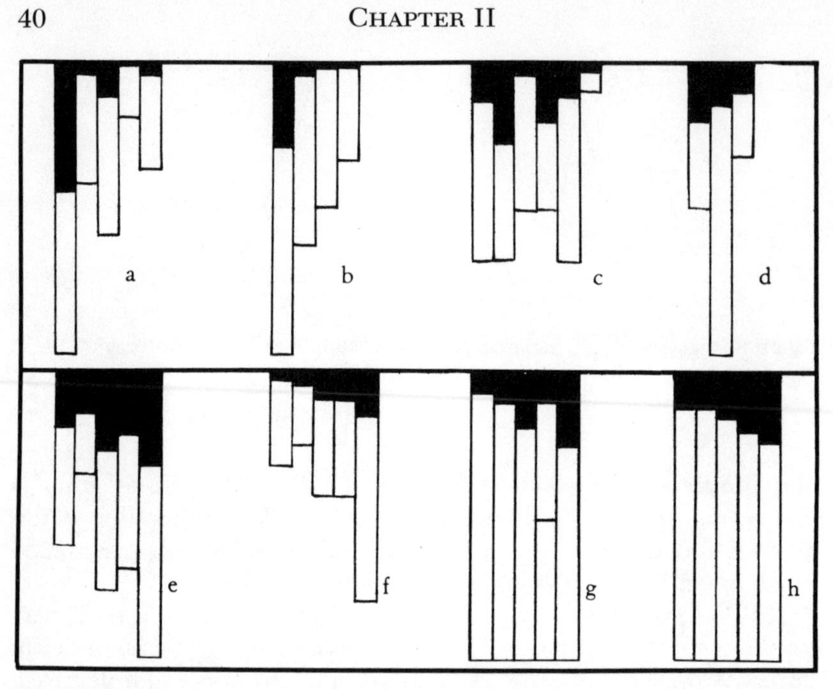

Figure 7. Composite progression histograms illustrating gain and decay series. Real gain: (*a*) pulsed, (*b*) linear. Artificial gain: (*c*) pulsed, (*d*) linear. Real decay: (*e*) pulsed, (*f*) linear. Artificial decay: (*g*) pulsed, (*h*) linear.

A. *Real gain series, pulsed.* In this series, gain is achieved by a convergence of the discussion on one topic, namely, the cell.

> Now the zygote to start out—each plant, each animal starts out as a single cell.
>
> You started out as a single cell, a zygote.
>
> Now mitosis is the process by which you became more than a single cell.
>
> Mitosis—you filled up with cells.
>
> First we'll have two cells.
>
> Then how many cells will there be?

B. *Real gain series, linear.* This closely integrated series with high commonality achieves gain by converging on the topic of arthropods.

> Many of these are beetles with very, very interesting colors.
>
> Some are flies and bugs.
>
> Everything there is an arthropod.

And this helps you realize the infinite variety of arthropods.

C. *Artificial gain series, pulsed.* Gain in structure is achieved here by introducing topics which are increasingly less potent, thereby masking the lack of convergence toward a single topic. Hence, the gain is artificial.

It's resistant to any and all changes, adverse changes in the environment, such as an extreme increase in temperature.

If the bacterium normally grows at room temperature—if you boil them, they will form an endospore.

---- Resistant to what?

Well, if you try to grow bacteria in an environment or in a media that does not supply all its requirements, well, some bacteria, those that don't form endospores, will die.

But some will form the endospores and remain in that form until the environment is changed so that it will support growth.

The, uh, resistant part of the endospore is the wall.

The wall of the endospore is the very rigid, very resistant part of the structure.

D. *Artificial gain series, linear.* As in the artificial pulsed gain series, this segment of discourse achieves gain in structure by masking the lack of integration among discourse units through a progression toward less potent material.

OK. There is no cellulose present.

Next we have the cell membrane.

And there is also something different about the cell membrane in bacteria.

And let's see if you can figure out what it is.

E. *Real decay series, pulsed.* The dashed lines enclose the limits of the series. The additional statements are included to demonstrate that a decay series is often employed as a terminal series in a span of discourse before entering into a new span with a different topic. Note how this sequence is dominated by divergence in the discourse rather than convergence.

Plasma can be divided into two parts.

For one thing, it has in it the platelets which cause the clotting of blood.

Platelets—and if platelets are removed from the plasma, what's eventually left is called serum.

These then are the three things that you could say make up the blood.

---- Uhm, what are erythrocytes again?

It's just another word for red blood cells.

Plasma consists of platelets plus serum.

Serum for sick people.

Let's go on now to talk about the functions of the blood.

F. *Real decay series, linear.* In this decay series, loss in structure is explained by the introduction of increasingly divergent verbal elements. Note that in contrast to a pulsed decay, the decline in structure here is much more gradual and less saccadic. The communication is divergent through the introduction of such diverse verbal elements as *digestive juices, stomach, digests, kills,* and *blood stream.*

What you might see happening is that the white cell moves in this way to surround this little bacterium.

So that eventually it completely surrounds it in this way.

And once it's surrounded it like this, it is able to send in digestive juices in a similar way the digestive juices are present in our stomach.

---- So it sort of just bottles it up?

Yeah and this just digests it.

It kills it and digests it.

---- So when the white blood cells attack germs they surround it?

They surround it and in that way, uh, eliminate it from the blood stream and kill it off.

G. *Artificial decay series, pulsed.* Decay is artificial in this series since there is no increase in unmatched elements toward the end; rather, the elements introduced are increasingly more potent. The same rationale is true for the next example.

Amphibians, anything else in this group?

---- Birds.

Birds, right.

Now are there any other groups that have backbones?

OK, with each of these groups then what we'll do is look at a couple of different characteristics in each one which again separates one from another.

I think you can see what we're doing; we started out with phyla, now we're looking at some classes.

H. *Artificial decay series, linear.* Decay is achieved in this communication by introducing highly potent verbal elements such as *biotic factors, ancestral influence,* and *inheritance.*

There are influences interculturally.

All right, but before we had communication—.

Now we'll go back and look at these different types of biotic factors in more detail.

First we'll look at the ancestral influence.

Later on this semester we'll talk about inheritance and genetics in more detail.

Symmetries

Three types of *symmetries* in communications have been identified thus far: (1) linear symmetry, (2) repeat symmetry, and (3) mirror symmetry.

A *linear symmetry* occurs when a plateau appears in a Kinetogram; all of the B_2 values are the same in the span. Symmetry is simply a construction in discourse where the second discourse unit is related to the first in the same way as the third unit is related to the second, and so on throughout the length of the span. Linear symmetries are classified by the number of points in the plateau. Two-point and four-point linear symmetries are shown in Figure 8. The corresponding discourse spans are presented here as illustrations A and B.

Figure 8. Two-point (*a*) and four-point (*b*) linear symmetries are shown as they typically appear in Kinetograms.

A. *Two-point linear symmetry.* The italicized statements are the ones forming the two points in the Kinetogram symmetry.

No, sea cucumber is under Molluscs also.

Those that have a kind of spiny covering are under Echinoderms.

No, sea urchin comes under here (*Molluscs*).

Barnacles come under here (Arthropods).

B. *Four-point linear symmetry.* The italicized statements form the four points. In this case the symmetry arises from all four having no elements in common when compared in pairs. Moreover, as is the case in most symmetries, there is an alternation in the topics discussed: *chromatids,* then *mistakes;* then *chromatids* and then *mistakes* again.

It should be an exact replication.

These two chromatids should be exactly the same as this chromosome.

You can have mistakes taking place here.

So they aren't the same. (referring to chromatids)

And you can also have mistakes taking place in the separation.

Well, you get an abnormality, and it all depends on what the abnormality is and how big it is what will happen.

Repeat symmetries occur when two or more identical forms appear in direct succession in a Kinetogram. The same pattern of organization is repeated in succession two or more times. Figure 9 illustrates a repeat symmetry, and corresponding verbal discourse is shown below. The dashed line indicates where the repeat series begins; it is almost identical to the preceding series in structure.

What are these (Abalone)?

---- Abalone.

Abalone, and where do they grow?

Pacific, yes, and we don't have these on the Atlantic coast as far as I know.

And this, this is the abalone with its native covering on—this outside rock covering.

The living animal of course is gone.

The living animal would be where my hand is.

And it's wonderfully adapted for its life in the very heavy surf and on the rocky coast of the Pacific Ocean.

It is fastened tight to the rock.

It resists being pushed around by the waves and so is a great example of a thing adapting to its biome.

A thing you use them for in the Pacific area is what?

Did you ever eat any abalone?

Mirror symmetries occur when a bilaterally symmetrical form appears in a Kinetogram span. In this construction, one half of the symmetry contains an organization of communication which is repeated in reverse order in the second half. The content may be different in the two halves, but the organization is a mirror-image relationship of the two. Figure 10 displays a mirror symmetry. Its corresponding verbal passage appears below. In this mirror symmetry, the organizational pattern of the first three discourse units is repeated in reverse order in the last three units. The fourth statement is the center point in the mirror symmetry.

So sodium is left without—with minus an electron.

What would happen to it?

---- Positive.

Charge is what?

---- Positive charge.

Charge is decreased, I mean increased because of this loss of a minus charge.

So you have a positive sodium.

It's lost one of its electrons so it has an extra positive charge.

Chlorine has gained an extra electron so we can see that it has a minus charge.

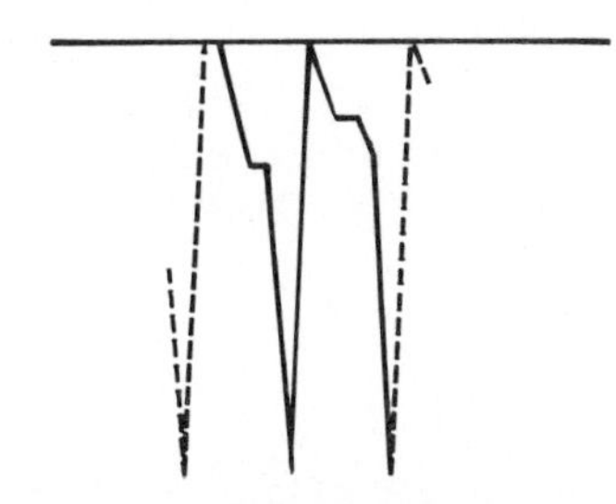

Figure 9. Kinetogram plot of a repeat symmetry.

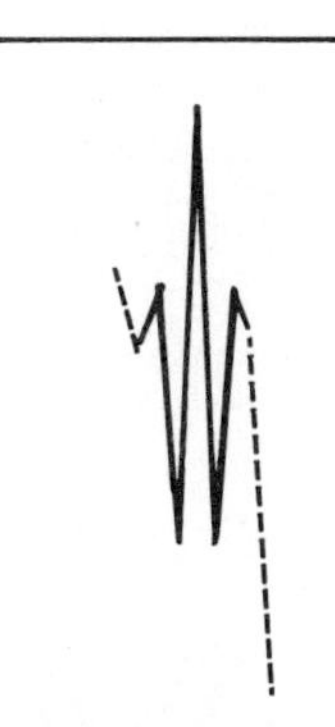

Figure 10. Kinetogram plot of a mirror symmetry.

CHART 1. PULSES, SERIES, AND SYMMETRIES SUMMARIZED

Kinetogram Form	*Description*
Narrow pulse	A sharp downward spike composed of only three defining points.
Broad pulse	A wide spike with more than three defining points.
Perfect pulse	One whose final anchor point is located on the abscissa; its coefficient of structure is unity.
Imperfect pulse	One whose final anchor point does not lie on the abscissa; the coefficient of structure for this point is less than unity.
Gain series	Any sequence in a Kinetogram where the trend of the points is upward. If it is composed of spikes, it is called a pulsed gain; otherwise, it is called a linear gain.
Decay series	Any sequence in a Kinetogram where the trend of the points is downward. If it is composed of spikes, it is a pulsed decay; otherwise, it is a linear decay.
Real series	Any of the above kinds of series whose B_1 values vary concomitantly with the B_2 values.
Artificial series	Any of the above kinds of series whose B_1 values *do not* vary concomitantly with the B_2 values.
Linear symmetry	A plateau of two or more points in a Kinetogram curve.
Repeat symmetry	Any series of points forming a repeating array of curves in the Kinetogram.
Mirror symmetry	A bilaterally symmetrical set of curves in a Kinetogram. A set of curves wherein one half of the set is a mirror image of the other.

As in the case of gain and decay series, the reality of all types of symmetries should be determined before classifying them. The B_1 values must follow the same pattern as the B_2 values plotted in the Kinetogram if the symmetries are real and not artificial. Artificial symmetries should be cited as a category separate from that of real symmetries. The latter are more clearly defined and their organizational patterns are more salient than in artificial symmetries.

The verbal examples given above—of gain series, decay series, and symmetries—illustrate the subtle differences in organization occurring in classroom communications. The significance of these organizational schemes for pupil knowledge acquisition has not been determined as yet. The fact is, however, that these patterns occur repeatedly in teaching; and their occurrence, relationships to one another, and significance in broader contexts of the total communication should be studied toward a complete understanding of the natural events of classroom communication.

The various kinds of pulses, series, and symmetries are summarized in Chart 1. Such structures are usually, but not always, contained within the longer sequences of discourse (primary and secondary spans) to be discussed in the following section.

Primary and Secondary Spans

A method of analyzing communications into sequences in terms of continuities and discontinuities in verbal content will be described and demonstrated in this section. The sequences thus identified are called primary and secondary spans. The method as applied in this investigation has resulted in analyses which effectively divide a communication into non-overlapping constituent parts which include all of its discourse units. These sequences, called *secondary spans,* are sometimes grouped together into longer sequences called *primary spans.*

The method involves simultaneous examination of a *code summary sheet,* displaying all of the code numbers assigned to each discourse unit of the lesson, and of the corresponding *Kinetogram trace.* When the analysis of a lesson is complete, the code summary sheet and Kinetogram are marked and labeled to show both the extent and the dominant verbal content of each span, as illustrated in Appendix A.

The continuities sought by the analyst in the identification of spans are of course functions of commonality. They consist of or are initiated by *connected sequences of discourse units*—series of units with internal coherence produced by overlapping or shared elements. One or more of these connecting elements may be clearly dominant in the sequence, occurring with high frequency and/or wide distribution. In other sequences, where matching elements keep changing more or less continuously, the identification of a "dominant" element may be somewhat arbitrary.

Spans begin at the beginnings of such connected sequences—when a new element or set of elements appears (either for the first time or after a period of inactivity) and either persists more or less continuously, or introduces a series with relatively high B_1 structure, or both. A span may extend beyond the continuity of the initiating sequence into a series of units with no discernible continuity, ending at the unit just prior to the appearance of a new connected sequence.

In examination of the code summary sheet, a connected sequence may not be readily visible if it does not include a "run" of dominant elements. But a spike in the Kinetogram is of course clear evidence of discontinuity produced by the activity of new and potent verbal content. Kinetogram spikes are therefore examined throughout the analysis, to discover or confirm span origins. Large-amplitude spikes often herald the onset of new primary spans; however, some spikes initiating primary spans may be relatively small because the new content is closely integrated with that of preceding units.

The transcript of the discourse should also be examined regularly to confirm the logic of span identifications. Moreover, if the signs in the code sheet or Kinetogram are ambiguous, then any teacher statement suggesting the beginning of a new discussion should be taken as a cue to begin a new span at that point. Obviously, however, there may be little interobserver reliability when the structure is so ambiguous as to require this subjective judgment.

Experience has shown that it is preferable to identify all secondary spans first and then, where possible, include these in primary spans. (In most cases, secondary spans should be at least four discourse units long; any series of fewer units should be included within a secondary span.) If there is continuity, through several secondary spans, of one or more verbal elements—even sporadic continuity, interrupted by long sequences in which the connecting element does not appear—the secondary spans are subsumed in a primary span.

Chart 2, "Rules for the Identification of Kinetogram Spans," specifies the criteria for the decisions to be made, with code summary sheet and Kinetogram at hand, beginning with the first few discourse units and thereafter whenever a new span origin is sought.

The application of these rules, and certain ambiguities that must sometimes be resolved, will be illustrated with reference to Figure 11, which displays a portion of a code summary sheet and a longer portion of the corresponding Kinetogram trace. (On the Kinetogram, vertical dashed lines show the beginning points of secondary spans.)

We see in units 1–9 of the code sheet a run of dominant element 7, which clearly constitutes a span or at least the beginning of one. The problem is where to end it. New element 10 and element 9 (which appeared once previously) appear in unit 9, where element 7 stops; but neither of these persists to establish a new run.

CHART 2. RULES FOR THE IDENTIFICATION OF KINETOGRAM SPANS

1. Examine the code summary sheet to determine if there is a connected sequence of discourse units containing a clearly discernible set of one or more dominant verbal elements. If such a series is identified, it constitutes a span and terminates when the dominant elements end and/or a *new* set of elements begins a new connected sequence. The new span begins at the discourse unit where the new connected series begins. The prior span is terminated at the discourse unit nearest to the beginning of the new span.

2. If no clearly discernible sequence of dominant elements is observed, then examine the Kinetogram to locate the first large-amplitude spike appearing therein. The new span will be initiated at that point if the code summary sheet contains evidence that the spike coincides with the onset of a connected series of discourse units. The distribution of overlapping or shared elements should produce a mean B_1 coefficient appreciably greater than zero for this series ($\bar{B}_1$ about 0.5 or better). This latter sign is used as a confirmation that the spike is initiating an identifiable, internally coherent discourse span.

3. If the conditions stated in item 2 are not satisfied, there may be a coupling between spans which obscures their limits. Under these conditions a new span may be initiated whenever a *new set* of highly integrated elements first appears in the code summary sheet. (A *new set* of highly integrated elements is a set of elements which, not contained in the preceding units of the span initiated earlier, are distributed in an overlapping pattern in the next several units.) This new span, once initiated, is terminated only when one or more of the criteria cited in items 1 and 2 are met.

4. Whenever a broad, blunt-tipped spike is used as a sign for the beginning of a span, it will usually be necessary to examine the code summary sheet in order to determine which point in the plateau of the blunt tip is the initiatory point for the span. In this case, the criterion of rule 1 is applied, and if a clearly dominant element first appears at some point within the spike, the new span is initiated at that point. If not, the first point in the plateau of the spike is used as the initiatory point.

Nor is there any other set of elements which are clearly dominant for four or more units beginning with unit 9 or 10. In the Kinetogram, however, a large-amplitude spike appears at unit 11. This coincides with the appearance of new elements and also introduces a sequence with high B_1 structure. Therefore the spike is taken as the major cue: the first span ends at unit 10, the next begins at unit 11.

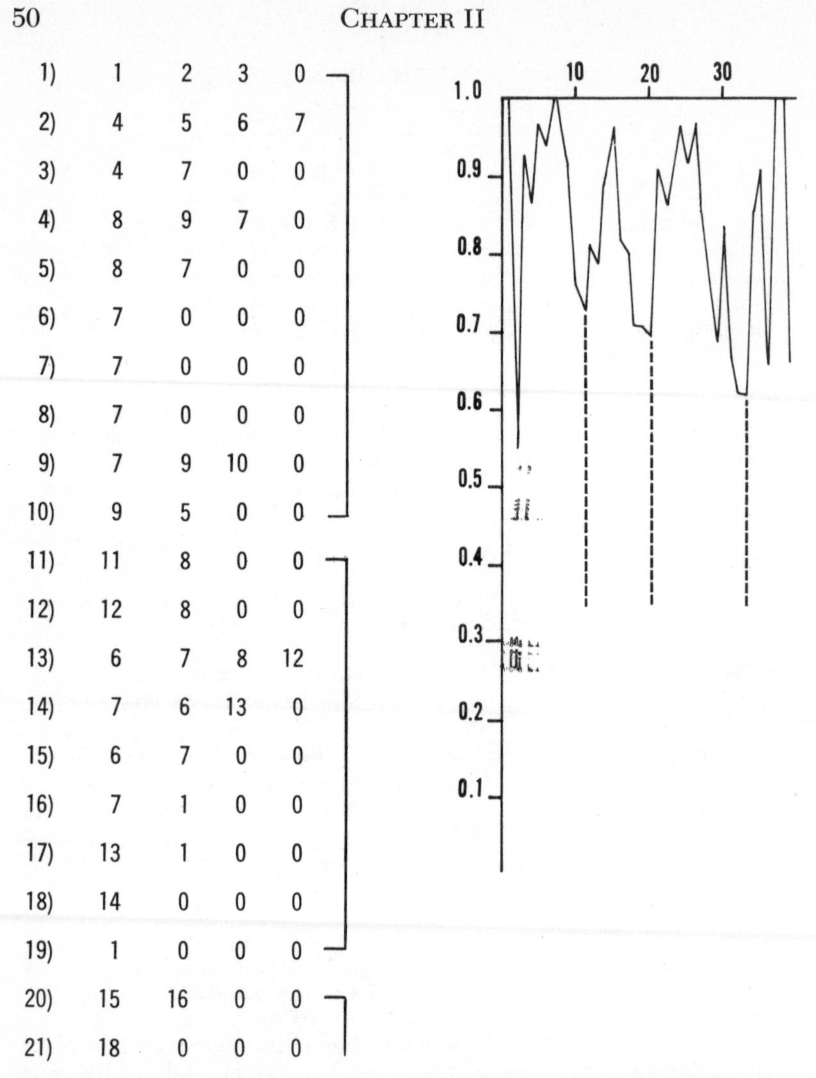

1)	1	2	3	0
2)	4	5	6	7
3)	4	7	0	0
4)	8	9	7	0
5)	8	7	0	0
6)	7	0	0	0
7)	7	0	0	0
8)	7	0	0	0
9)	7	9	10	0
10)	9	5	0	0
11)	11	8	0	0
12)	12	8	0	0
13)	6	7	8	12
14)	7	6	13	0
15)	6	7	0	0
16)	7	1	0	0
17)	13	1	0	0
18)	14	0	0	0
19)	1	0	0	0
20)	15	16	0	0
21)	18	0	0	0

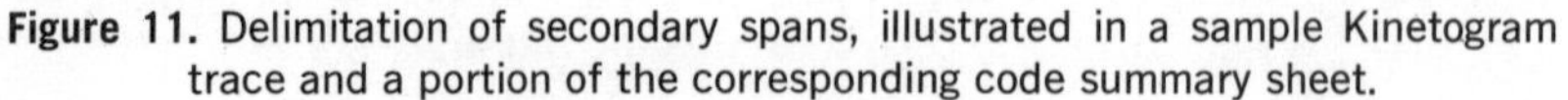

Figure 11. Delimitation of secondary spans, illustrated in a sample Kinetogram trace and a portion of the corresponding code summary sheet.

Now, where does the second span end? Once again there is some ambiguity, partly because there is no clear run of any single element whose termination we might use as a cue. However, the continuous overlapping of elements ends with units 18, 19, and 20; moreover a large-amplitude Kinetogram spike occurs here. Therefore the second span ends at unit 19 and the new one begins at unit 20.

The span originating at unit 20 is terminated at unit 32, corresponding to the first point of a large blunt spike, because a new set of elements begins a clear run at its second point, unit 33, initiating a new span.

Further details involved in span identification will be illustrated in the following description of the spans shown in a complete code summary sheet and corresponding Kinetogram for Transcript T-A (see Appendix A). On the code sheet, each bracketed span is labeled with the names and code numbers of its dominant verbal elements as determined by highest frequency of occurrence in the span and/or widest distribution throughout the span. (If there are several elements with highest frequency, the one most widely distributed is chosen as dominant. If there is also no choice in this respect, the first of the highest-frequency elements to occur is designated.) The labels for these elements, together with their frequencies in the span, also appear on the Kinetogram.

Looking at the code sheet in Appendix A, we see that the first four discourse units are clearly dominated by code numbers 5 and 6. At the fifth unit, there is a beginning of a long sequence dominated by code number 13. This unit is confirmed as a span origin by a large-amplitude spike located at point 5 in the Kinetogram. Therefore, the first four units are bracketed as a secondary span. The labels *horny, 5* and *structure, 6* are written at the right of the bracket as identification for the span.

The fifth through the thirteenth discourse units contain numerous references to mammals (element 13), and this element continues very active after unit 13. However, a new element (code 27) which also is very active in the next few units appears at unit 14. Hence two brackets are drawn with their boundaries corresponding to the three major Kinetogram spikes at points 5, 14, and 20. The labels *mammals, 13* and *warm-blooded, 27* are affixed to these two spans. The next discernible span, a very short one, contains two references to *body temperature, 34.* It is delimited by the major spike at unit 20 and a much less prominent spike at point 23 on the Kinetogram. (The reader is cautioned to note that this small spike is characteristic of those occurring when linkage is present between spans. Verbal element 27 spills over into the new span, as a "coupler" of one of the types to be described in detail later. But for that, the spike at unit 23 would have deepened to a longer one at unit 24, where new elements initiate a new span.) The short span begun at unit 24 concludes at 33, just before a major spike at unit 34.

A careful perusal of the series of secondary spans beginning at unit 5 and ending at 33 will confirm that verbal element 13 is dominant and is sufficient cause to bracket the whole series as a primary span, labeled *mammals, 13*. The origin and conclusion of this span obviously correlate with two major spikes on the Kinetogram.

The next span, dominated by elements 52 and 53, is a secondary span that stands alone, not part of a larger span. It extends from unit 34 to unit 39.

Discourse unit 40 initiates another series of secondary spans subsumed within a primary span. The span is initiated at unit 40 because element 28 originates there and has a high frequency of occurrence in subsequent units. The secondary span initiated at unit 40 terminates at unit 52. This is determined by the onset of high activity for the new element *bat, 62*. Moreover, sharp spikes occur at units 40 and 53, as is expected when there is no coupling and a new span begins. At discourse unit 60, a new secondary span is initiated when the element *warm-blooded, 27* appears. The origin of the next secondary span is determined by the appearance of the element *feet, 59* at discourse unit 65. This element persists throughout the next several discourse units including unit 74. However, the next span (which is part of a new primary span) does not begin until unit 76, where element 82 begins a high-frequency run and where a large spike appears in the Kinetogram. Therefore, the secondary span labeled with element 59 ends at unit 75. This also terminates the primary span.

In the next primary span, the first secondary span (labeled *reptiles, 82*) is concluded at discourse unit 81, whereafter a clear run of high frequency appears for verbal elements 87 and 88. This secondary span is terminated at discourse unit 86, since element 82, included within the large blunt spike at units 86–87, initiates a high-frequency run at 87. Moreover, the next few discourse units (87–92) have high commonality. This example illustrates a situation where there is some uncertainty about the origin of the new span and where the onset of a new element within a large-amplitude spike is sufficient evidence for the beginning of the span at that point. The final secondary span within the primary span is a long one, beginning at discourse unit 98, which contains the first of two consecutive appearances of element 31 and coincides with a spike in the Kinetogram. This point, moreover, initiates a sequence with continuously overlapping content which ends only at unit 109. The high commonality is produced by several short sequences integrated in turn by high-frequency elements 39, 98,

43, and 45. *Heart, 39* is the first of the two highest frequency elements to appear, and is also widely distributed in the span.

Unit 109 is the first point of a large blunt spike whose second point, unit 110, introduces the dominant element 84 of the final, free-standing secondary span.

As illustrated in these examples, primary spans are identified as long sequences of discourse wherein some verbal element occurs with sufficient frequency and distribution to set a series of secondary spans apart from the preceding and following spans. The primary span usually begins where the distinguishing element first appears and is terminated when the last secondary span is terminated within that series.

The analyst should always be alert to find new ways of detecting structured spans of discourse in otherwise seemingly disorganized communications. Such innovations, when shown to be reliable, will be welcome additions to the literature.

Transitions Between Spans

A method of classifying transitions and assigning quantitative values to certain couplings between spans will be described in this section. Several definitions of terms will be needed before the procedures are outlined.

The length (*S*) of a primary or secondary span is the number of discourse units it contains. The word *span* designates not only a sequence of discourse units but also the length of such a sequence. In the code sheet shown in Appendix A, the first secondary span has a span (length) of 4. The primary span following it extends from unit 5 through unit 33; its span is 29.

The terminal sections of two spans being analyzed in terms of transition (the end part of the first and the beginning part of the second) will be called *terminal spans* and identified as follows: The number (*S*) of units in the span is divided by 4, and the quotient (rounded to the nearest whole number) is called the *quarter-span.* To determine the number of units in the terminal span we use either the quarter-span or the number 4, whichever is smaller. Thus, in a span containing 20 or 21 discourse units, the quarter-span is 5, and, since 5 is greater than 4, the terminal span consists of 4 discourse units in this case. If the span contained 8 or 9 units, then the quarter-span would be 2 and the terminal span would have only 2 units because 2 is smaller than 4. In a span containing only 4 or 5 units, the terminal span would be simply the first (or last) unit of the span.

The concept of *mixing* among verbal elements is important for the analysis of couplings and other transitions in communication. Brief definitions and examples of such transitions have been given in Chapter I; these concepts will be fully developed here and further discussed with reference to quantification.

Mixing occurs when the terminal spans of contiguous primary or secondary spans contain some verbal elements in common and when the spill-over elements from one span occur in discourse units interspersed with units containing elements specific to the other span. Often there is spill-over of elements from one span to the next *without* mixing.

Sometimes a discourse unit contains *only* elements spilled-over from the contiguous terminal span. However, if a spill-over unit *also* contains elements *not* spilled-over but belonging more specifically to its own span, the unit is called an *internal couple.*

If an internal couple is the *first* unit of a span, this *does not* constitute mixing. If such an internally coupled first unit has some elements in common with the last unit of the prior span, the two units together are a *coupled pair;* again, this is not a case of mixing.

Any spill-over unit, whether internally coupled or not, which occurs *after* the first unit of a span *does* constitute mixing.

To clarify these definitions, symbolic examples are presented. A slash is used to denote the beginning of a new span. Dotted vertical lines mark the limits of terminal spans. The letters A and B represent discourse units and the verbal elements contained in them. When an internal couple occurs—that is, a unit containing both element A and element B—it is symbolized as –A,B–.

The first illustration is a simple case of mixing. The second discourse unit in the second span contains only A, which is a spill-over from the previous span, and is preceded and followed by units containing B:

· · · A—A—A—¦A—A—A—A— / B—A—B—B¦—B—B · · ·

The following illustration is not a mixed state. There is an internally coupled discourse unit in the second span. Moreover, the two italicized units in the array constitute a coupled pair. However, since the internal couple is the first unit in the second span, this is not a case of mixing.

· · · A—A—A—A—¦A—A—A—*A*— / *A,B*—B—B—B¦—B—B · · ·

If an internally coupled unit appears *after* the first introduction of a new verbal element, this does constitute mixing. It is called, specifically, mixed-mode coupling. Note in the next example that the internal couple A,B occurs after element B is introduced in the second span.

· · · A—A—A—|A—A—A—A— / B—A,B—B—B|—B—B · · ·

Chart 3, "Key to Transition Types," has been devised for the precise identification of certain transitions called *couplers.*It is assumed that primary or secondary spans have been identified and their terminal spans marked in some way. It should be noted that in the identification of couplers, *only* the contiguous *terminal spans* are examined for common elements. Later, *if* couplers are discovered, the occurrence of the coupling elements throughout the primary or secondary spans is noted and the frequencies used in computing a quantitative measure of coupling.

CHART 3. KEY TO TRANSITION TYPES

Non-coupled Transition (NC). Contiguous terminal spans contain no verbal elements in common. There is no mixing. There are no internally coupled discourse units.

Loose Coupler (C-1). Contiguous terminal spans contain verbal elements in common. There is mixing. There are no internally coupled units.

Close Coupler (C-2). Contiguous terminal spans contain verbal elements in common. There is no mixing. The first discourse unit in the second terminal span is internally coupled.

Mixed-mode Coupler (C-3). Contiguous terminal spans contain common verbal elements. There is mixing. An internally coupled unit appears somewhere in the second terminal span.

When the type of transition between two contiguous spans has been identified, a *terminal activity coefficient* (*TAC*) is computed if the transition is a coupler. This coefficient is the ratio of the frequency of occurrence of the coupling elements in the terminal spans as compared to the frequency of their occurrence in the total spans. As an example, assume that a C-1 coupler occurs between two spans and that verbal element 3 was the only mixed element. Further assume that element 3 occurred 4 times in the combined terminal spans and a total of 12 times in the two complete spans. The *TAC* then is $4/12$, or 0.33. The *TAC* is a measure of the terminal activity of coupling elements. If *TAC* is unity, it means the coupling elements occur only in the terminal spans and therefore serve specifically as a terminal device to integrate the two spans of discourse. The closer *TAC* approaches zero, the less concentration of the coupling elements in the terminal spans and the greater their distribution through the complete spans.

When a C-2 or C-3 coupler is identified, the analysis may be refined to determine how the coupled verbal elements in the internally coupled discourse unit are related to one another. If the elements merely appear in the same unit without being equated or assigned to the same class of phenomena, the coupling is called *incidental* and a 1 may be added to the code symbol. Thus, C-2:1 and C-3:1 are respectively C-2 and C-3 couplers with incidental coupling of verbal elements. If, however, the internally coupled discourse unit contains a statement equating the coupling elements or assigning them to the same class of phenomena, this is called an *identical* coupling and may be assigned the code symbol C-2:2 or C-3:2. Since decisions about incidental and identical coupling often require subjective judgments, they should be applied with great caution.

To further illustrate the analysis of transitions, the code sheet and the corresponding Kinetogram summary table exhibited in Appendix A will be used. The primary and secondary spans will be referred to by their index numbers, which appear in the summary table but not on the code sheet.

The first two primary spans are non-coupled (NC), and therefore no *TAC* can be computed. The second and third primary spans are coupled with a mixed-mode coupler (C-3) whose *TAC* is 0.75.

Secondary spans 2 and 3 have a mixed-mode coupler (C-3). The terminal spans are the last two units (12, 13) of span 2 and the first two units (14, 15) of span 3. The only verbal element appearing in both terminal spans is element 13. Its frequency in the terminal spans is 2; in the total spans together, 11. *TAC* for these spans therefore is $2/11$, or 0.18.

A C-2 coupler occurs between secondary spans 3 and 4. Terminal spans are the last two units of span 3 and the first unit of span 4. Again element 13 is the only common element. But this time the internal couple in which it occurs is the first unit of span 4; there is no mixing.

Another C-2 coupler occurs between secondary spans 4 and 5. Again there is only one common element: 27. $TAC = 2/3$, or 0.67.

Neither here in primary span 1 nor elsewhere in this entire lesson are there any C-1 couplers.

Kinetogram Summary Table

The features of matching-element structure in a communication may profitably be gathered into a Kinetogram summary table containing the following items:

1. Mean fundamental coefficient ($\bar{B}_1$).
2. Mean weighted coefficient ($\bar{B}_2$).
3. Total number of discourse units.
4. Total activity (Σf) of all verbal elements.
5. Number of primary spans and their mean span length.
6. Number of secondary spans, including those within primary spans, and their mean length.
7. Summary description of each primary span, in terms of dominant element(s), mean B_1 and B_2 coefficients, transition type, and *TAC* where computable.
8. Summary description of each secondary span, as for primary spans.
9. Summary description of gain and decay series, symmetrics, static-structure series, and high-kinetic-structure series: origin and conclusion; mean B_1 and B_2 coefficients.
10. Percentage distribution of B_1 values in 0.1 unit intervals.
11. When appropriate, relative activity histograms demonstrating cascaded chain series should be appended, with a list of the verbal elements being cascaded. (See pages 39–40 and page 84 of *Structure in Teaching.*)

A summary table for the Kinetogram of Transcript T-A is also exhibited in Appendix A.

Additional results of Kinetogram analyses will be presented in Chapter III.

Method Stability and Reproducibility

The mean amplitude of the spikes in a Kinetogram is inversely related to the value of Σf (total frequency of all elements) for the lesson. Longer lessons will have higher mean B_2 coefficients and therefore, on the average, lower amplitudes $(1 - B_2)$—shorter spikes and more elevated peaks. But the essential *shape* of a Kinetogram—the distribution and relative proportions of its spikes and peaks—is *not* affected by the length of the lesson. This is a very important stability property which allows accurate comparisons to be made between lessons of different length.

We may clarify the relationship as follows. For a given ordered set of B_1 coefficients and F' and F'' values (as for all the unit pairs in a lesson), a given constant value of Σf will produce a certain set of B_2 coefficients which in turn produce the spikes and peaks of a certain Kinetogram. With the *same* set of B_1 and F values, a *different* value of Σf will produce a different set of B_2 coefficients and a different Kinetogram—different in mean amplitude but *not* different in form. Since $1 - B_2$ varies inversely with Σf, spike amplitudes—*all* of them—will decrease as Σf increases. (The relationship is of course curvilinear, being negatively accelerated. In general, therefore, a point will be reached where mean amplitude no longer decreases appreciably as Σf increases.)

The problem of comparison does not arise in connection with mean B_1 coefficients, of course, since the length of the lesson is not a factor in the individual B_1 values.

To demonstrate that the length of the lesson also has no effect on the essential form of its Kinetogram, Figure 12 shows Kinetogram spans plotted for the same sequence of discourse using different values of Σf (varying from 100 to 600 in intervals of 100). Although the amplitudes of the spikes decrease, on the average, as Σf increases, the form of the graph remains unperturbed. Moreover, the mean amplitudes stabilize to a fair degree when Σf reaches 400 or greater. This is the range typically achieved in lessons of 30 to 40 minutes in length.

As an aid in computing approximate values of B_2 and in comparing Kinetograms, a graph (Figure 13) has been assembled showing the quantitative relationships among the variables contained in the equation for the weighted coefficient of structure (B_2). These variables are B_1, B_2, $(F' + F'')$, and Σf. The ordinate contains B_2 values, and the abscissas contain B_1 values. There are six abscissas, labeled 100, 300, 400, 500, 600, and 700, each representing a Σf value. For example, if an unknown variable is to be determined for a communication wherein Σf is 500, then the abscissa labeled with 500 is used as a reference axis. The convergent set of lines bearing the labels 1, 4, 8, 12, 16, 30, 50, 75, and 100 represent values of $(F' + F'')$. Thus, if an unknown variable is to be determined for a communication where the pair of discourse units being analyzed has $F' + F'' = 12$, then the line labeled with a 12 will be used in identifying the coordinate representing the value of the unknown variable. As an example, suppose one wished to determine the approximate value of B_2 for a pair of discourse units in a communication where $B_1 = 0.4$, $(F' + F'') = 8$, and $\Sigma f = 300$. The abscissa labeled *300* should be located, the coordinate corresponding to $B_1 = 0.4$ is identified, and its intercept with the

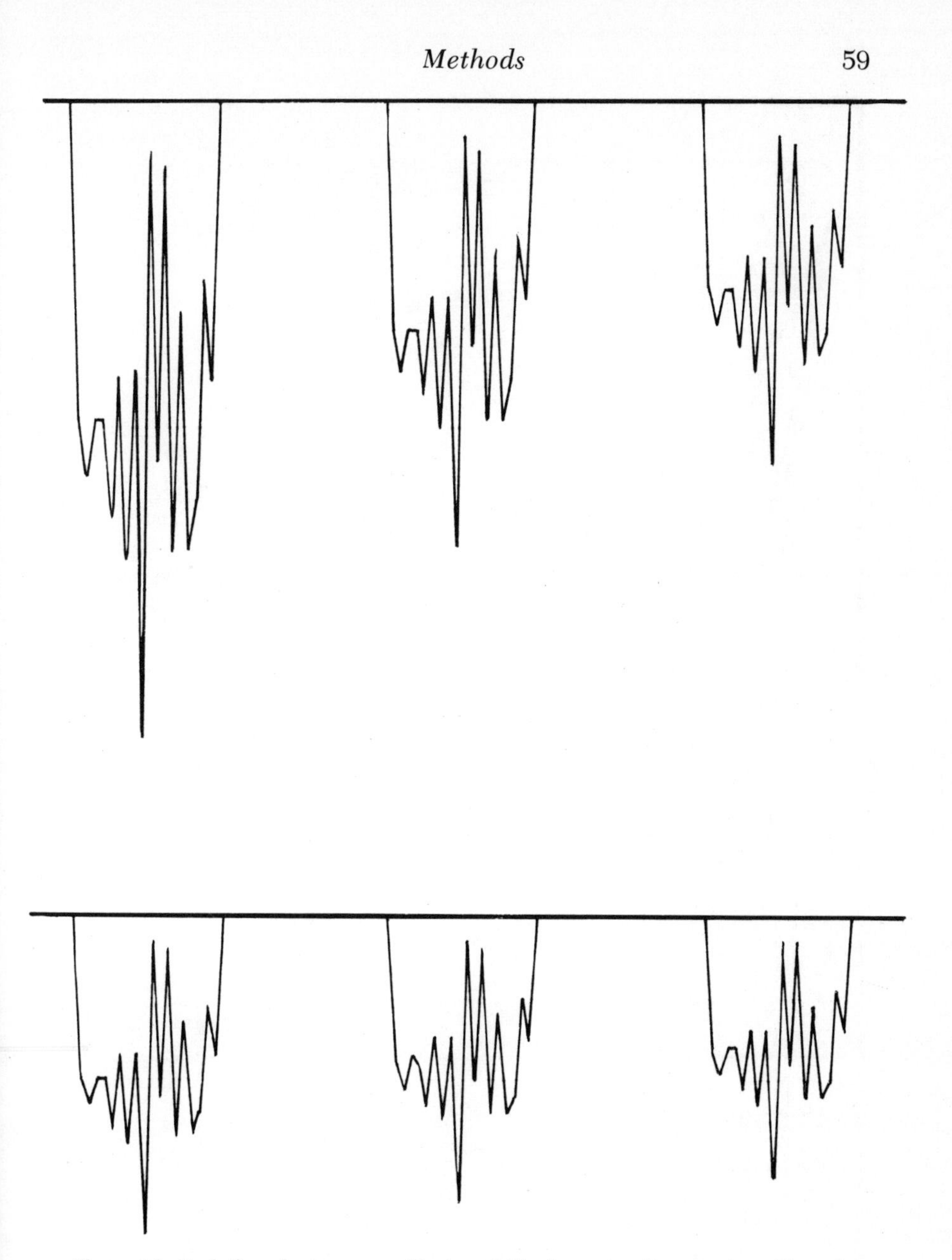

Figure 12. Variations in mean amplitudes of Kinetogram spikes produced by using different constant values of Σf in computing B_2 values.

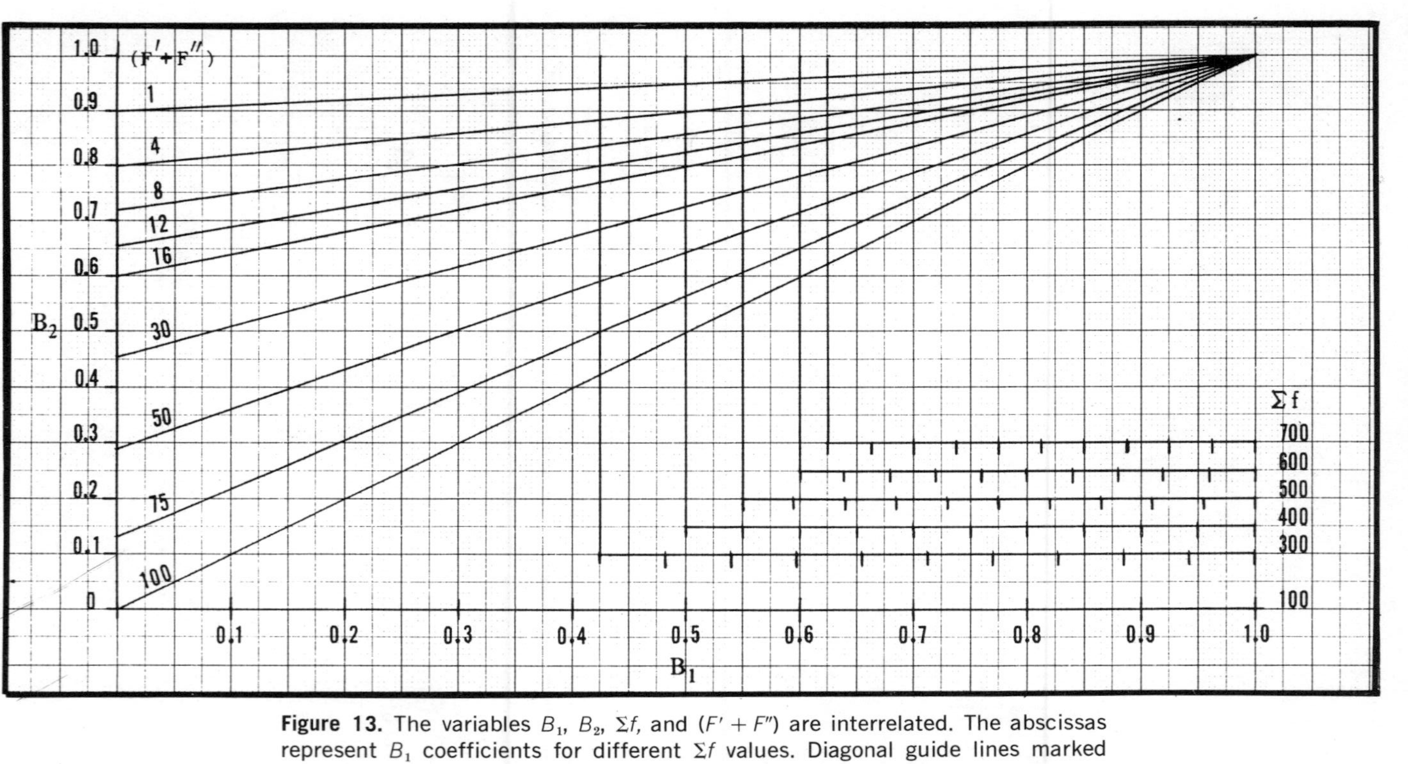

Figure 13. The variables B_1, B_2, Σf, and $(F' + F'')$ are interrelated. The abscissas represent B_1 coefficients for different Σf values. Diagonal guide lines marked $(F' + F'')$ are used in locating approximate B_2 values corresponding to specified B_1 values. B_2 values are read on the far-left ordinate.

line labeled 8 marks the point horizontally on the extreme left-hand ordinate equivalent to the desired B_2 value; namely, $B_2 = 0.9$. When necessary, approximations can be made by interpolating reference points between the various lines contained in the graph.

The use of this graph in converting $\bar{B}_2$ values to a standard form, for the comparison of spans in different lessons, is described and exemplified in Chapter III.

To give further aid in achieving reproducible results, the mean number of verbal elements and mean number of discourse units emitted by a teacher during each minute of a lesson are presented in Table 1. These values were computed from seven different lessons by diverse teachers in both the physical and biological sciences. The values can be used as guides in predicting how long one must record a lesson to obtain a given number of discourse units or total verbal element frequency. The standard deviations are also given in Table 1.

TABLE 1. MEAN NUMBER OF DISCOURSE UNITS AND MEAN FREQUENCY OF VERBAL ELEMENTS EMITTED EACH MINUTE OF CLASSROOM DISCOURSE

	Mean Number of Discourse Units	*Mean Frequency of Elements*
Grand Means for All Conditions	7.76 ± 0.99	17.50 ± 2.10
Means for Low Pupil Interaction*	8.23	18.42
Means for High Pupil Interaction**	6.34	15.19

Pupil statements / Teacher statements = (0.21)* and (0.48)**

The number and kinds of verbal elements coded will of course be critical in determining the amplitudes of spikes and the form of the curves in the Kinetogram. In general, the best rule to apply is to code all words falling within the categories of (1) high frequency within the communication, and (2) technical words in the substantive field being communicated. If this rule is applied generously rather than parsimoniously, as specified earlier, highly reproducible results should be obtained. The list of coded elements in Appendix A should also be reviewed as a guide in the identification of suitable kinds of words for coding.

To demonstrate the effects of idiosyncrasies in coding on the form of the Kinetogram, the same span of discourse units was coded three ways, with variations in the number and kind of words coded. In the first list, only the most obviously technical words were coded;

in the second, additional technical words were added; and in the third, all words used with high frequency as descriptive terms as well as all discernible technical words were coded. Figure 14 shows the three corresponding Kinetogram sequences in the aforementioned order. The stability and robustness of the method against such minor idiosyncratic errors is evident.

The main difference is in fine structure. To gain the most information, therefore, a reasonable generosity in coding is recommended. It is obviously fallacious and deleterious to code such common words as *is* and *can,* since these occur so frequently as to obscure the major patterns of organization among substantive elements. A careful analysis of the transcript should be made to identify all technical words and their synonyms as well as any substantive and descriptive words used with high frequency. Too parsimonious coding will tend to elevate the mean fundamental coefficient. Unless gross errors are committed during coding, however, such changes in $\bar{B}_1$ values will be slight.

In the coding stability studies performed thus far, undercoding as described in the above examples and illustrated in Figure 14 produced a range in $\bar{B}_1$ values from 0.32 to 0.34. This .02 variation (which, though not trivial, is very small) was produced by reducing the number of elements in the code list by 17 per cent. Of course this stability property does not justify careless or incomplete coding of discourse units. Omissions and improper assignment of code numbers can alter the Kinetogram record, and presumably could cause erroneous identification of span limits. Once a list of code elements has been compiled, careful attention must be given to their proper identification in each discourse unit.

Finally, to demonstrate formally that the method of analysis using the Kinetogram is assessing organized patterns in communication and not merely random patterns, a series of random numbers was compiled approximating the length and range of values found in coded transcripts. The Kinetogram produced from this input contained few spikes, and there were long spans of undifferentiated straight lines. The mean fundamental coefficient was 0.033. These data clearly show that the methods reported here are measuring other than random inputs when communication is the object of analysis.

Paper-and-Pencil Computation of Coefficients

When computer facilities are unavailable, a convenient hand method for computing B_1 and B_2 values can be used in conjunction with Figure 13. In this method, the audio record of the dis-

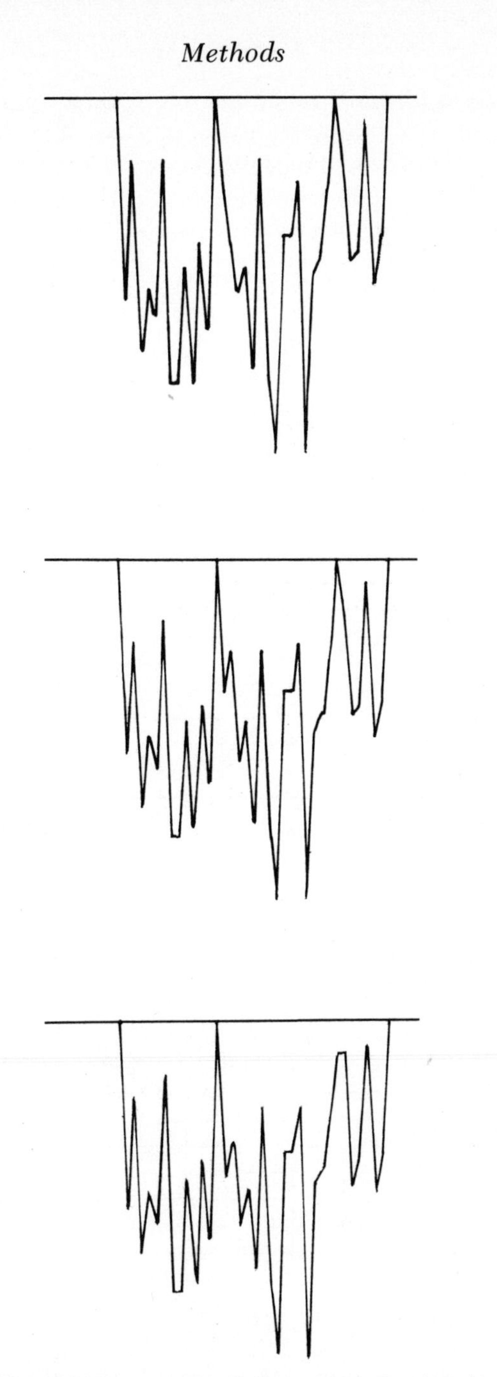

Figure 14. The effects of idiosyncrasies in the coding of verbal elements are illustrated in the corresponding Kinetogram traces.

course need not be transcribed prior to the analysis of the communication. A record is kept of the occurrence of verbal elements in each discourse unit by marking squares on a code summary sheet as shown in Chart 4. Only a section of a complete chart is reproduced to illustrate the method.

CHART 4. HAND COMPUTATION OF B_1 AND B_2 COEFFICIENTS

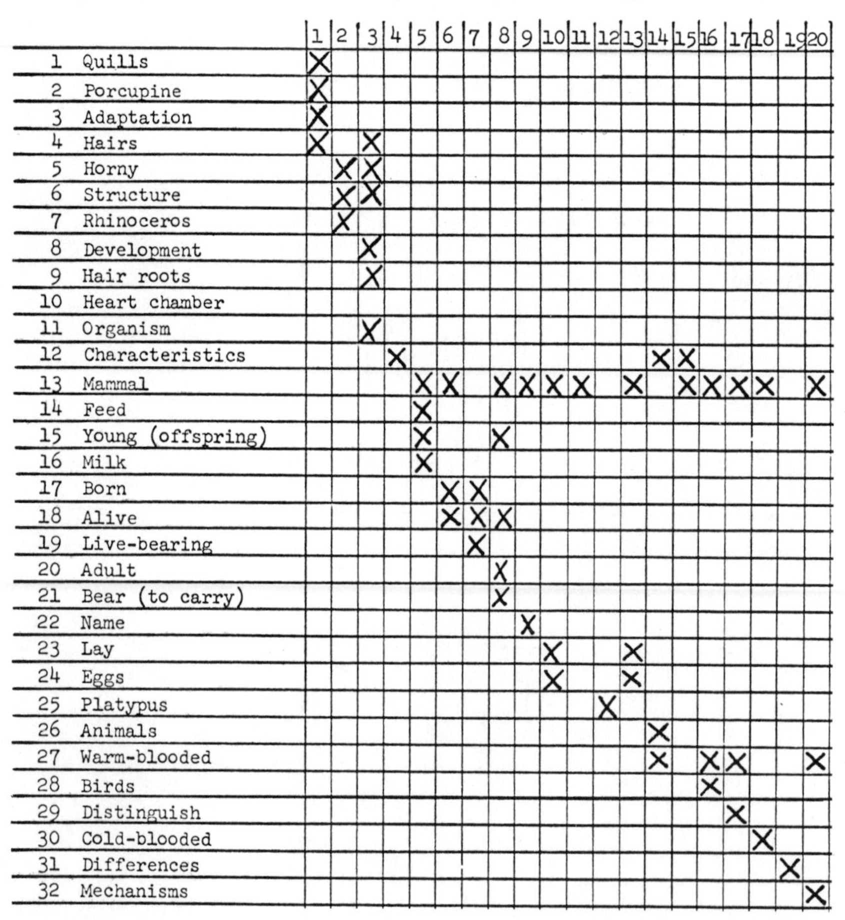

VERBAL ELEMENTS	1	2	3	4	5	6	7	8	9	10	11	12	13	14	15	16	17	18	19	20
1 Quills	X																			
2 Porcupine	X																			
3 Adaptation	X																			
4 Hairs	X		X																	
5 Horny		X	X																	
6 Structure		X	X																	
7 Rhinoceros		X																		
8 Development			X																	
9 Hair roots			X																	
10 Heart chamber																				
11 Organism			X																	
12 Characteristics				X										X	X					
13 Mammal					X	X		X	X	X	X		X		X	X	X	X		X
14 Feed					X															
15 Young (offspring)					X			X												
16 Milk					X															
17 Born						X	X													
18 Alive						X	X	X												
19 Live-bearing							X													
20 Adult								X												
21 Bear (to carry)								X												
22 Name									X											
23 Lay										X			X							
24 Eggs										X			X							
25 Platypus												X								
26 Animals														X						
27 Warm-blooded														X		X	X			X
28 Birds																X				
29 Distinguish																	X			
30 Cold-blooded																		X		
31 Differences																			X	
32 Mechanisms																				X

(Column headings: DISCOURSE UNITS)

The left-hand column contains a list of verbal elements to be coded. This list can be compiled ahead of time by reviewing the taped lesson or by securing a list of terms from the teacher prior to the recording period. The latter method is of dubious value, since many unpredicted terms always appear in the lesson. As a precaution, blank spaces can be left between the entries in the left-hand column, thereby allowing room for additional terms to be added as the lesson is monitored. Alternatively, the verbal elements can be listed during the time that the lesson is being analyzed. Each term is listed as it appears for the first time in the discourse. A check mark is placed in the appropriate discourse unit square the first time an element is heard in each unit. As shown in Chart 4, each discourse unit is represented by a column. All verbal elements in discourse unit 1 are marked in column 1. The remaining columns are marked as each discourse unit unfolds in the communication.

When all columns have been marked and the audio record is exhausted, the total frequency of check marks in each row is determined. Each row sum represents the activity of an element. The total activity (Σf) for the entire lesson is the grand sum of the row totals. The B_1 coefficients are computed by examining the number of matching elements in each pair of columns divided by the total number of verbal elements marked in the two columns. In Chart 4, columns 1 and 2 contain no matching check marks; therefore $B_1 = 0$. In columns 2 and 3, however, elements 5 and 6 are matched, thus yielding four matched check marks out of a total number of nine marks in the two columns. The B_1 coefficient is, therefore, $4/9 = 0.44$. This procedure is repeated for each consecutive pair of columns until the total communication has been analyzed. The B_1 values are customarily listed at the bottom of each column, starting with the second.

The B_2 value for each pair of columns is computed by using the graph in Figure 13. The abscissa to be used is determined by the Σf for the total communication. Each pair of columns is then examined to determine which unmatched element in each of its columns has the highest frequency in the total lesson; for the first column of the pair, this is F'; for the second column, F''. The sum $(F' + F'')$ for each pair of columns in succession must be computed. These values will determine which diagonal line in the graph (Figure 13) is to be used as a guide in locating the approximate B_2 value on the left-hand ordinate. Each B_1 value is located on the appropriate abscissa and its intercept with the appropriate diagonal line is determined; the B_2 value on the ordinate corresponding to this point of intersection is then determined. It is convenient to produce an ordinate on a separate piece of graph paper and slide this across the graph to quickly determine where the diagonal line and the abscissa coordinate intersect with reference to the values on the ordinate. It is sometimes difficult to follow the lateral lines across the graph because of the several diagonal lines running across them. Therefore, the separate ordinate allows one to move the ordinate scale directly onto the particular abscissa being used in the analysis.

As an example, assume the lesson recorded in Chart 4 has a total activity of 300. The first pair of columns have $B_1 = 0$ and $F' + F'' = 9$. The abscissa on the graph marked 300 is used for all calculations in this lesson. The origin of this abscissa is of course the point where $B_1 = 0$. Now the diagonal line marked 8 comes closest in numerical value to the $(F' + F'')$ factor. The B_2 value corresponding to the intercept of these two lines is 0.84. When all of the B_2 values have been determined by this method, they can be plotted to yield a Kinetogram. The code summary sheet is used to detect sequences of one or more dominant elements as an aid in the identification of primary and secondary spans. The remaining analyses are performed as explained earlier in this chapter.

Analysis by the Serial Comparison Method

In the serial comparison method, a coefficient of structure (B^0) is obtained by comparing the serial order of the discourse units in a communication with the serial order of discourse units in a criterion sequence. The coefficient so obtained gives the correlation between a criterion dimension and a communication sequence. The criterion sequence must contain the same content as the communication; only the sequential order can be different. (In a strictly controlled experiment comparing the two sequences, the actual statements, as well as their essential content elements, should be identical.) If the communication contains maximum kinetic structure with reference to the criterion sequence, the two sequences are either identical in all respects or identical in terms of their essential verbal content.

A criterion sequence based on the commonality of verbal-element content in contiguous discourse units can be produced by rearranging a given communication sequence, beginning with the second discourse unit, until all of the units have been ordered so that contiguous discourse units have the maximum possible number of verbal elements in common. Thus, a criterion sequence is one whose commonality among discourse units is maximum with reference to that set of units and when the first discourse unit is taken as the beginning of the criterion sequence. A criterion sequence produced in this way can be used to compute B^0 for a given communication by comparing the rank order of the discourse units in the criterion sequence with the order contained in the communication under analysis.

A computer program is available from the author to produce criterion sequences of the sort just described. The program first rearranges the input array to produce a new array whose sequential order is based on the following criteria:

1. The first discourse unit as represented by its code numbers is taken as the initial value in the new array.
2. All discourse units with the same codes as the first are located and listed next, in the same order as in the old array.
3. The next discourse unit selected is the one containing the most elements in common with the previous unit. When this nearest-match discourse unit has been added, all of its code-identicals are located and listed in the same order of occurrence as in the original communication.
4. This process is repeated until all of the discourse units available in the input array are rearranged.
5. If a point is reached during the compiling of the new array where no matching discourse units can be located, then the very next unused discourse unit is taken and the process is begun again.

When the new array has been compiled by the computer, it performs a second task of computing the B^0 coefficient for the input array, based on the comparison of serial order between the input array and the new criterion. Additional print-out is given on the total ordinal deviation (*sum deviate*) of the new array when compared to the input. The *interchange,* or total number of items rearranged, is also printed. The serial comparison method is a convenient device to determine how closely the organization of a communication approximates an ideal sequence based on maximum commonality among the discourse units contained therein. Since the computer program is a sorting process, it can be quite slow when long series are being analyzed. If computer time is precious, only short sequences such as individual primary spans should be analyzed by this method. In some lessons analyzed previously using the method for the total communication, the values of B^0 obtained ranged from 0.24 for a high-static-structured lesson to 0.40 for a high-kinetic-structured lesson.

The serial comparison method may also be used to assess kinetic structure based on explicitly spatial or chronological order of discourse units, without reference to their verbal commonality. This use of the method is described in *Structure in Teaching* (pages 24–25, 30–31, and Appendix A).

CHAPTER III

Analyses

In this chapter, each of six science-content classroom transcripts will be analyzed. Comparative analyses will be performed at the conclusion of the chapter.

The presentation for each communication will be based on these materials as shown in the Appendices: (1) Kinetogram summary table; (2) Kinetogram; and (3) table of fundamental coefficients, B_1. When appropriate, selected portions of the audio transcript will be displayed to clarify the interpretations of the corresponding signs in the Kinetogram. Each transcript and its Kinetogram is designated by the letter *T* and a number, thus: T-1, T-2, and so forth. Kinetogram T-1 will be analyzed in greater detail than subsequent ones; and its full transcript, list of coded elements, and code summary sheet are exhibited as appendices as an aid to the reader in acquiring analytical and interpretive skills.

In all Kinetograms, vertical solid lines mark the limits of primary spans; the length of the span is represented by a horizontal arrow-tipped line extending between the solid vertical lines. The numerical index of the span appears beneath the horizontal line. The secondary spans, either those contained within primary spans or those free standing, are set apart by dashed vertical lines. The dominant verbal element and its activity within the span are shown. For example, *egg, 30:6* means that the verbal element *egg* (code number 30) appeared six times in the span.

References to specific discourse units in a communication are made using the abbreviation D.U. and the index number of the discourse unit. The first discourse unit in a communication is symbolized as D.U. 1. A range of discourse units is cited by giving the limits of the sequence; for example, D.U. 7–12 means discourse units 7 through 12 inclusive. Verbal elements of discourse units will be cited by name and code number.

The *specificity* of a verbal element in a given span of discourse is the ratio of its activity (frequency of occurrence) in the span to its total activity in the whole communication. When an element occurs exclusively within a specified span, the coefficient of specificity is unity. The specificity coefficient is an index of activity distribution for a given element or set of elements. If half of the total activity of the element occurs in a given span, then the specificity index relative to that span is 0.5.

Secondary spans vary in the amount of *theme activity* they contain. A *theme* will be defined as a persistent, dominant verbal element whose recurrence throughout a span of discourse provides a continuous thread of thought. Some secondary spans exhibit high theme activity; that is, there is a continuous activity of a single element or set of elements throughout the span. Other spans have little persistent activity of any single verbal element; their theme activity is low.

A convenient measure of theme activity in a span is the *relative activity coefficient* for the dominant element in the span. The relative activity coefficient (*RAC*) is computed by dividing the frequency of occurrence of a verbal element in a sequence of discourse units by the number of units in the sequence. If a span contains a highly active element, then the relative activity coefficient for that element will approach unity. If, however, no individual element gives coherence to the span, the *RAC* for any given element will be considerably less than unity.

An interesting characteristic of a communication is the extent to which the relative activity coefficients of the dominant elements in the secondary spans correlate with the mean fundamental coefficients for these spans. The question to be answered is: To what extent do secondary spans with high mean fundamental coefficients also contain a theme as determined quantitatively by the numerical value of the relative activity coefficient? To answer this question for a given transcript, the mean fundamental coefficients ($\bar{B}_1$) and relative activity coefficients (*RAC*) for all secondary spans may be plotted as a scatter diagram, and the degree of correlation is determined by using the *sample correlation coefficient* as applied by

Snedecor and Cochran (29, p. 160). A positive correlation will indicate that communications with high theme activity tend to have higher mean fundamental coefficients than those with low theme activity.

Analyses of Individual Transcripts

Transcript T-1

This communication is addressed to the general topic of interaction among living organisms and their relationships to the environment. The Kinetogram, Kinetogram summary table, table of B_1 values, code summary sheet, list of coded elements, and the coded transcript itself are displayed in Appendix B.

The first primary span, D.U. 1–35, contains six secondary spans clearly organized with reference to a spatial dimension. The discourse proceeds according to a spatial organization beginning with a discussion of the atomic and molecular levels of biological structure and extending up through tissue, organ, and organismic levels. The first primary span, therefore, is dominated by content labeled *levels of biological organization.* This class of verbal elements includes the following: *interaction, 4; atoms, 7; cells, 13; cellular reticulum, 15; tissues, 24;* and *organism, 32*. The specificity for this class of elements in the first primary span is 0.54. This means that over one-half of all the activity of these verbal elements in T-1 was contained in the first primary span. The remaining activity for these elements is distributed non-specifically throughout subsequent primary spans. An artificial pulsed decay series concludes the first primary span. The mean fundamental coefficient for this primary span, $\bar{B}_1 = 0.39$, lies close to the mean for the total communication, $\bar{B}_1 = 0.41$. In five of the six secondary spans contained in the first primary span, $\bar{B}_1$ is 0.42 or higher. Each of these secondary spans is clearly initiated by a large amplitude spike in the Kinetogram, thus providing salient limits for each secondary span.

The second primary span of T-1 contains a presentation of content about environmental and biotic influences on living organisms, D.U. 36–104. The seven internal secondary spans contain no discernible spatial or chronological dimensions. This means there are no clearly discernible references to objects in a spatial array or events in a temporal sequence. The mean fundamental coefficients for the seven internal secondary spans vary from $\bar{B}_1 = 0.17$ to $\bar{B}_1 = 0.53$. Only two of the spans, however, exceed the mean fundamental coefficient for the total lesson. The first and second primary spans are coupled by a C-2 coupler containing two coupling elements in the coupled pair of discourse units: *species, 33* and *offspring, 38*. These are paired in the communication with *population growth, 40,* the new element in the beginning of the primary span. Static structures appear in the spans of D.U. 86–93 and D.U. 97–104. The specificity of verbal elements in the second primary span is 0.82; hence, 82 per cent of the total activity of the dominant elements (*population growth, 40; death rate, 42; birth rate, 43; biotic factors, 70;* and *plants, 1*) is contained within the second primary span. The remaining activity for these elements is non-specific in the remaining spans of the communication.

The third primary span, with topics on man, culture, and inheritance, contains three secondary spans. The first and third secondary spans have mean fundamental coefficients of $\bar{B}_1 = 0.30$ and $\bar{B}_1 = 0.21$ respectively, which are lower than the mean fundamental coefficient for the total communication. The mean weighted coefficient of the second secondary span is $\bar{B}_2 = 0.95$, a value considerably higher than the mean for the whole communication, indicating that this is a high-kinetic-structured sequence. The primary span is initiated with a C-3 coupler whose $TAC = 0.63$, which means that 63 per cent of the coupler's activity occurs in the terminal segment of the span. This is appreciably higher than the TAC of 0.33 for the C-2 coupler initiating the second primary span. The fourth primary span begins with a C-3 coupler and the last is non-coupled (NC).

The fourth primary span, D.U. 132–193, contains five secondary spans. The discourse is dominated by the verbal element *bird, 82,* whose coefficient of specificity is 0.82. Three of the five secondary spans have $\bar{B}_1$ values greater than the mean coefficient for the total communication.

There are four free-standing secondary spans in the next discourse sequence, D.U. 194–226. They include diverse dominant elements: *learning, 81; population, 39; environment, 3;* and *species, 33.* The mean fundamental coefficients are $\bar{B}_1 = 0.43$ or higher in all of these spans.

The final primary span, D.U. 227–267, is dominated by a discussion of population and crowding. The specificity for the combined verbal elements *man, 78* and *crowding, 152* is 0.72. There are six internal secondary spans with a range of mean fundamental coefficients varying between $\bar{\bar{B}}_1 = 0.31$ and $\bar{\bar{B}}_1 = 0.68$. Three of the six internal secondary spans have $\bar{B}_1$ values exceeding the mean for the whole communication.

A free-standing secondary span concludes the communication and is dominated by the verbal element *ethology, 140*. The mean fundamental coefficient for this span is $\bar{B}_1 = 0.5$.

The correlation for the *RAC* and $\bar{B}_1$ values of the secondary spans of transcript T-1 (as plotted in the scatter diagram of Figure 15) is $r = 0.65$. This is significantly different from zero with $p < 0.01$. These data support the generalization that spans of discourse dominated by a theme tend to achieve higher commonality than those without a mediating theme. This is not a tautology, since it is possible to achieve high commonality without a theme. In fact, some of the secondary spans in T-1 are so organized, as evidenced in part by two scatter diagram points falling clearly to the lower right of the main trend of points.

The coefficient of agreement among four coders for the limits of the secondary spans was 0.90 when the rules given in Chapter II were applied.

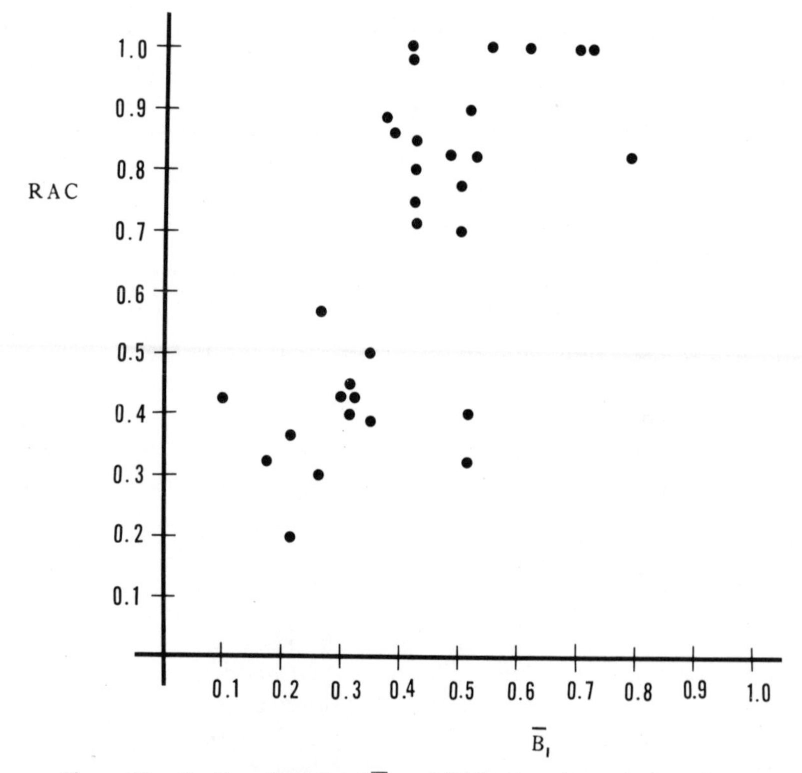

Figure 15. Scatter diagram of $\bar{B}_1$ and *RAC* values in secondary spans of Kinetogram T-1.

Transcript T-2

This communication on the topic of bacteriology (Kinetogram and related materials in Appendix C) terminates with two clearly discernible primary spans. The remaining discourse is organized into free-standing secondary spans. The whole communication is dominated by the verbal element *bacteria, 1.* The specificity of the dominant verbal elements in the primary spans is 0.93 (*nucleus, 32*) in D.U. 123–147 and 1.0 (*endospore, 77*) in D.U. 148–175. The sequence of secondary spans beginning at D.U. 66 and terminating at D.U. 147 is interesting; it is based on a spatial dimension wherein the components of a bacterial cell are presented beginning with the most exterior component, the capsule, and progressing inward culminating with a discussion of the central nuclear material. The second span, D.U. 10–14, is dominated by a four-point linear symmetry. The discourse concerns the nomenclature of rod-like bacteria called bacilli. The ninth secondary span, D.U. 66–82, contains a high degree of kinetic structure as demonstrated by the mean fundamental coefficient ($\bar{B}_1 = 0.60$), which is higher than the mean coefficient for the total communication ($\bar{B}_1 = 0.44$). The discourse in this sequence is concerned with the function of the slime capsule in the maintenance of bacterial life.

The fifteenth span, D.U. 148–161, contains an artificial pulsed gain series. The saccadic organization of the discourse in this pulsed span can be observed in the following transcript segment.

149.	What's an endospore?	78
150.	An endospore is the technical name for it.	77
151.	And it's a very resistant structure.	77, 85, 25
152.	Resistant to any and all changes, adverse changes in the environment such as an extreme increase in temperature.	85, 72, 73
153.	If the bacterium normally grows at room temperature – if you boil them they will form an endospore.	1, 73, 77
----	. . . bacteria . . . water on it . . .	
154.	Right. Well, also, if it, if you try to grow bacteria in an environment or in a media that does not supply all its requirements, well, some bacteria, those that don't form endospores,will die.	1, 72, 74, 77, 75
155.	But some will form the endospores and remain in that form until the environment is changed so that it will support growth.	77, 72, 76

156. The, uh, resistant part of the endospore is the wall. 85, 77, 35

157. It has, the wall of the endospore is the very rigid, very resistant part of the structure. 35, 77, 25, 85

158. And one other characteristic of endospores is that they can be located, they can be formed in various parts. 77

159. They can be formed at the end and therefore it's called a terminal endospore. 77

160. Or it can be formed—end, terminal—endospore because it's— 77

---- End of what?

161. End of the cell. 27

A scatter diagram showing the relationship between *RAC* and $\bar{B}_1$ values for secondary spans is presented as Figure 16. The correlation is $r = 0.34$. This is not significantly different from zero ($p > 0.05$). Since the primary spans are short and subsume only a

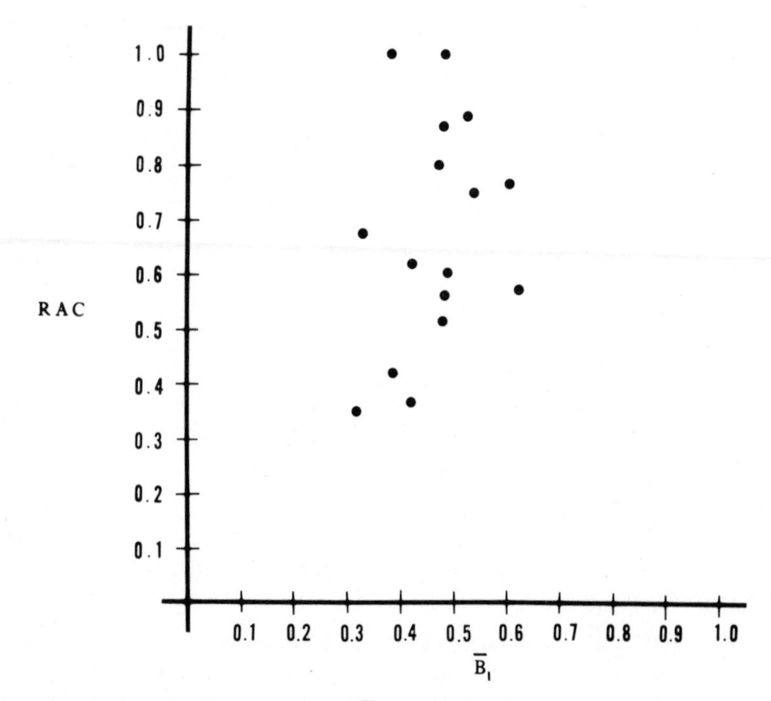

Figure 16. Scatter diagram of $\bar{B}_1$ and *RAC* values in secondary spans of Kinetogram T-2.

small proportion of the total number of secondary spans, the specificity of dominant elements was computed for the secondary spans as presented in Table 2. There is a clear tendency toward specificity in most of the spans whose coefficients are 0.5 or greater.

The coefficient of agreement among four coders for the limits of the secondary spans as presented here was 0.93.

TABLE 2. THE SPECIFICITY OF DOMINANT ELEMENTS IN SECONDARY SPANS OF TRANSCRIPT T-2

Secondary Span	*Elements*	*Specificity*
1	Leeuwenhoek, 3	1.00
2	Bacteria, 1	0.08
3	Cohn, 82	1.00
4	Unicellular organism, 7	0.22
5	Virus, 18	1.00
6	Microscope, 20	0.75
7	Bacillus, 11	0.50
	Spirilla, 23	1.00
	Cocci, 22	1.00
8	Structure, 25	0:29
	Cytoplasm, 26	0.33
9	Bacteria, 1	0.21
	Capsule, 38	1.00
10	Cell wall, 35	0.67
11	Cell membrane, 33	0.78
	Mitochondrion, 44	1.00
12	Cytoplasm, 26	0.58
13	Chromosome, 62	0.29
14	Nucleus, 32	0.29
	Molecule, 65	1.00
15	Endospore, 77	0.65
16	Spore, 70	1.00
	Endospore, 77	0.35

Transcript T-3

This communication on bacteriology contains three primary spans and eighteen secondary spans; eight of these are free standing. The dominant verbal elements in the primary spans and the specificity of each are, in order of occurrence: *heat, 8,* 0.94; *refrigeration, 42,* 1.0; *glycolysis, 105,* 0.91. It is interesting to note that *temperature, 7* occurs exclusively in the first and second primary spans, with specificity respectively 0.44 and 0.56. The first two secondary spans, with limits D.U. 1–21, contain a static-structured sequence, namely D.U. 1–12, followed by an artificial gain series,

D.U. 13–16, and finally a real pulsed decay series, D.U. 17–21. A succession of two-point linear symmetries is embedded within the aforementioned real pulsed decay series. This sequence of organization recurs in the fifth secondary span, D.U. 32–54. There is a static-structured series in D.U. 32–46 and then a brief high-kinetic-structured sequence D.U. 47–49. A real decay series terminates the span. There is a tendency for some of the secondary spans to begin with a gain series and terminate with a decay series, as exemplified here:

Secondary Span Limits	*Gain Series*	*Decay Series*
D.U. 92–109	92–95	102–109
D.U. 132–139	132–134	135–139

The specific attributes of each span can be ascertained from the Kinetogram and the Kinetogram summary table in Appendix D.

The coefficient of correlation between *RAC* and mean B_1 values of secondary spans is $r = 0.63$. This is significantly different from zero ($p < 0.01$).

The coefficient of agreement among four coders was 0.94 with reference to the limits of the secondary spans contained in transcript T-3.

Transcript T-4

This communication on animal classification contains six primary spans and thirty-five secondary spans. The high specificity of the dominant verbal elements in the primary spans is shown in Table 3. The Kinetogram and related materials are presented in Appendix E.

TABLE 3. THE SPECIFICITY OF DOMINANT ELEMENTS IN THE PRIMARY SPANS OF T-4

Primary Span	*Dominant Element*	*Specificity*
1	Coelenterates, 4	0.73
2	Flatworms, 51	0.83
3	Roundworms, 64	1.00
4	Molluscs, 82	0.93
5	Annelids, 120	1.00
6	Arthropod, 7	0.93

The mean length of the secondary spans is nine discourse units. There are several interesting organizations among these various spans. The sixth secondary span, D.U. 29–35, is dominated by pulses, whereas the seventeenth span, D.U. 106–128, is peculiar in having a linear symmetry at its beginning. The eighteenth secondary span, D.U. 129–145, contains exclusively a three-fold repeat symmetry. Static-structured series appear in D.U. 238–247, where the various characteristics of exoskeletons are being presented, and in D.U. 264–272, where the characteristics of arthropods, arachnids, and insects are compared.

The correlation between *RAC* and mean B_1 values of secondary spans for T-4 is $r = 0.47$. This is significantly different from zero ($p < 0.01$).

Transcript T-5

There are four primary spans in this communication on animal classification. (See Appendix F.) The specificity for the dominant verbal elements in the primary spans is 0.44, 1.00, 0.46, and 0.80. The first primary span is dominated by two verbal elements, namely *animal, 1* and *specimen, 2.* In this part of the lesson, the students are shown various forms of preserved animals. The second primary span is dominated by the element *name, 29;* in it the teacher discusses the importance of systematic methods of naming living things. Invertebrate *animals, 1,* are discussed in the third primary span. The following elements are exclusively specific to the third primary span: *echinoderm, 75; mollusc, 77; earthworm, 93; hookworm, 96; flatworm, 98; coelenterate, 105.* The fourth primary span is dominated by a discussion of *chordates, 68* and their phylogenetic (evolutionary) development. The content is organized progressively beginning with a presentation of the simpler forms followed by the more complex members of the group.

A higher incidence of pulsing and static structuring occurs in the second primary span, in D.U. 37–63, as compared to the other spans. This multi-relational discourse is consistent with the observation that the teacher is building up a concept or static structure of the meaning of scientific names. The discourse corresponding to this segment of transcript T-5 is presented here to illustrate the organization of this static-structured series.

37.	A similar thing happens if we use common names of plants and animals.	28, 5, 1
38.	An example that's given in your book concerns the maple.	6, 32
39.	The red maple is known in various parts of the country by different common names.	33, 30, 28

40.	One of these is called the soft maple.	28, 34
41.	Another of these is the water maple.	28, 35
----	Sugar maple . . .	
----	Red maple . . .	
42.	No, that's a different name.	33, 36
43.	Now suppose this maple, suppose you had a spot in your yard where you wanted to plant a red maple. The tree that you know of as the red maple.	32, 33, 37
44.	And you were discussing this idea with another person, who said, "No, I think a soft maple would be a good tree there."	34, 37
45.	Well, here you are talking about the same tree but using different names.	37, 38, 39, 29
46.	And it leads to a great deal of confusion.	39, 29, 40
47.	Uhh, in order to cut down on this confusion, a Swedish scientist whose name is given to you in your book– Does anyone remember his name?	40, 6, 29, 41
----	Luigi–	
----	Luigi? No.	
48.	A man by the name of Linnaeus developed a naming system which has been used ever since.	42, 43
49.	That involves giving each individual organism two names.	43, 44, 29
50.	Because there are two names, it is called the binomial.	29, 45
----	Should we write this down?	
51.	Yeah, this is the binomial system. The binomial system of naming organisms.	45, 29, 44
52.	Now if you look in your book, certain examples are given there.	6
53.	Uhh, if we consider the maple tree that we are talking about here, the red maple–	32, 33
----	This is the one that's called by two different names?	
54.	These two names are what make up the scientific names, what people call the scientific names.	29, 27, 44, 1, 5
55.	They all have some kind of scientific name.	1, 5, 27
56.	If you discover something new and it hasn't a name, you can give it a name according to this particular system.	29, 45

57. Now here's the scientific name for maple tree: *Acer* is the name given to any kind of maple, whether it's sugar maple or red maple, regardless of the kind of maple you're talking about. — 27, 32, 46, 36, 33
58. It has this first part, *Acer*. — 29, 46
59. Now it's in the second part that you get your various kinds of difference between the various kinds of maples. — 39, 29, 32
60. *Rubrum* means red maple. — 47, 33
61. For the sugar maple you would have the same *Acer*, then you would have *Saccharum*. — 36, 46, 48

---- Begins with a Z.

62. No, this is the sugar maple. — 48, 36
63. This is the red maple. — 47, 33

Secondary spans 6 and 7 are contained in this sequence of discourse. Their mean B_1 and B_2 coefficients are shown in the Kinetogram summary table of Appendix F. They are among the lowest values in the whole table, thus adding strength to the conclusion that this sequence is static-structured.

The correlation coefficient for *RAC* and mean B_1 values of all secondary spans is $r = 0.30$. This is not significantly different from zero ($p > 0.05$).

Transcript T-6

This communication on the topic of atomic structure and the periodic table in chemistry produced a Kinetogram (in Appendix G) containing four primary spans and twenty secondary spans. The specificity of the dominant elements in the four primary spans, in consecutive order of occurrence, is 0.43, 0.57, 0.55, and 0.58.

The Kinetogram trace forms two distinct linear series. One occurs at D.U. 40–60 and the second appears at D.U. 110–130. The structure of the communication in these series can be determined by examining the list of B_1 values in Appendix G. It is immediately apparent that these sequences contain little commonality among discourse units since most of the B_1 values are zero. When, however, a series of B_1 values greater than zero occurs, they are all of the same value or nearly so. The Kinetogram trace corresponding to these points is elevated. Examples appear at D.U. 47, 114–116, and 120–122 in Kinetogram T-6. We can conclude that in this communication extended linear series represent discourse series with little change in commonality. In large measure, ideas are presented as isolated units, but at those points in the Kinetogram where the trace courses upward, there is a brief sequence of consistently high commonality.

A salient characteristic of this communication is a high incidence of pulsing and static structuring. A consistently high recurrent activity throughout the communication for element *electron, 16* may account for part of the static structure. The repetitive appearance of *force, 2* and *electron, 16* throughout secondary spans of the communication is illustrated in a relative activity histogram (Figure 17). Mean B_1 values for secondary spans range from $\bar{B}_1 = 0.06$ to $\bar{B}_1 = 0.50$. The kind of discourse associated with static-structured sequences can be ascertained from the following excerpt corresponding to the static-structured series in D.U. 139–150.

139.	Chlorine as our original example will have a greater ability to gain another electron than sodium.	14, 16, 19, 34
----	Is electronegativity ability to . . .	
140.	Right, the ability to attract an electron to its nucleus.	18, 16, 45
141.	And you can just see, the electron dot configuration is a good way to associate this, since it's just dealing with outermost shells.	7, 17
142.	The chlorine has seven electrons in its outermost shell.	14, 16, 17

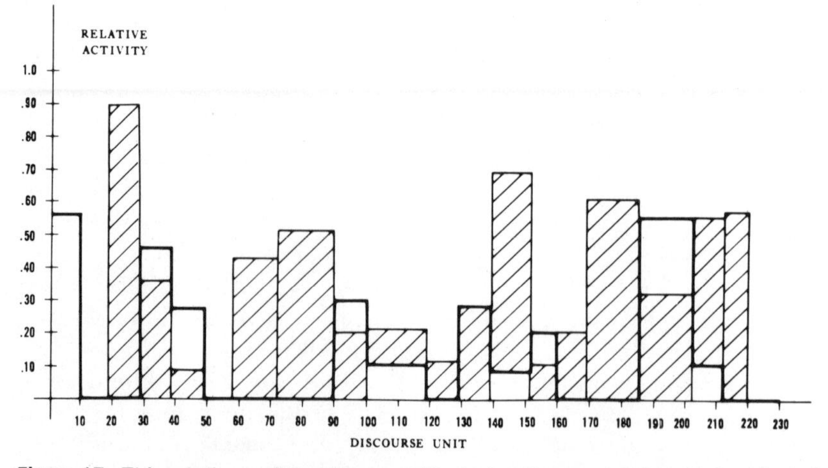

Figure 17. This relative activity histogram illustrates the recurrent and intermingled activities of verbal elements *electron* (black bar) and *force* (white bar) as they occur in Kinetogram T-6. The intermingled activity of these two verbal elements may account for part of the high pulse density and static structures present in Kinetogram T-6.

143.	There's going to be a greater electrostatic force.	28
144.	And it's going to want to acquire an electron much more than sodium would, OK?	34, 14, 16, 19
145.	Sodium, because its force is so low, sodium would tend to give off this electron.	34, 16, 2, 57
146.	And because of these great extremes from one side to the other, for instance form the sodium to the halogen family, these tend to combine very readily.	61, 15, 58
147.	One wants to give up an electron very readily.	57, 16
148.	One wants to gain.	25, 19
149.	And it's due to this ability, its ability to gain electrons.	16, 19
150.	OK, this is just a term for this ability, OK?	16, 19

The coefficient of correlation between *RAC* and mean B_1 values of secondary spans in transcript T-6 is $r = 0.54$. This is significantly different from zero ($p < 0.05$).

Comparative Analysis of the Transcripts

All of the science communications analyzed are composed of primary and secondary spans. In some cases, there was evidence for tertiary spans, but only primary and secondary spans will be analyzed. In transcripts T-2, T-4, and T-5, the primary spans are all contiguous, whereas the remaining transcripts contain some free-standing secondary spans interspersed among primary spans.

All of the communications except T-5 contain some couplers between primary spans. The couplers are predominantly C-2 and C-3. In Kinetogram T-1, a C-2 coupler links the second primary span to the first. The coupling element is *species,* 33. An examination of discourse units 35 and 36 in transcript T-1 as presented in Appendix B will illustrate how the teacher used the coupler as a transition between the two spans. The *TAC* for this coupling element is 0.33. This is not a very specific coupler, since only one third of the activity occurred within the terminal spans. A C-3 coupler links primary spans 2 and 3. The *TAC* is 0.63, a much larger value than that of 0.33 for the C-2 coupler. The coupled element in this mixed-mode coupler is *man,* 78, which is the dominant element in the first secondary span within the third primary span. The coupled element in the C-2 coupler linking the third and fourth primary spans is *inherit,* 74. A similar C-2 coupler occurs in Kinetogram T-2 at the transition between primary spans 1 and 2. The coupled element is *bacteria, 1*, a rather persistent element throughout the whole communication. It is not surprising that the *TAC* is 0.27, showing that less than one third of the coupled element's activity within the pair of spans occurs in the terminal spans. Kinetograms T-3 and T-4 contain C-3 couplers, whereas Kinetograms T-5 and

TABLE 4. DESCRIPTIVE DATA FOR TRANSCRIPTS T-1 THROUGH T-6

	T-1	*T-2*	*T-3*	*T-4*	*T-5*	*T-6*
	Mean Fundamental Coefficients					
	0.41	0.44	0.38	0.38	0.32	0.32
	Mean Progression Densities and New Activity Coefficients for the Total Communications					
	0.49 (0.7)	0.38 (0.6)	0.74 (1.1)	0.67 (0.9)	0.68 (0.9)	0.75 (0.9)
	Mean Progression Densities and New Activity Coefficients for Secondary Spans					
1.	1.06 (1.4)	0.43 (0.9)	0.60 (0.9)	0.86 (1.0)	0.79 (1.0)	0.42 (0.5)
2.	0.20 (0.4)	0.10 (0.2)	0.68 (1.1)	0.10 (0.2)	0.42 (0.6)	0.91 (0.9)
3.	0.61 (0.7)	0.17 (0.3)	0.71 (1.4)	0.63 (0.8)	0.97 (1.2)	0.34 (0.6)
4.	0.77 (1.3)	0.14 (0.3)	0.73 (1.0)	0.38 (0.7)	0.44 (0.6)	0.80 (1.2)
5.	0.50 (0.5)	0.34 (0.5)	0.60 (0.8)	1.72 (1.8)	0.04 (0.1)	0.85 (0.9)
6.	0.53 (0.9)	0.34 (0.6)	0.77 (1.1)	0.65 (0.9)	0.87 (1.2)	1.44 (1.5)
7.	0.15 (0.2)	0.10 (0.4)	0.67 (1.0)	1.18 (1.4)	0.78 (0.9)	0.37 (0.6)
8.	0.50 (0.7)	0.63 (0.9)	0.38 (0.6)	1.20 (1.4)	0.69 (0.9)	0.44 (0.5)
9.	0.96 (1.1)	0.29 (0.5)	0.96 (1.5)	1.00 (1.0)	1.00 (1.0)	0.98 (1.1)
10.	0.74 (0.9)	0.19 (0.4)	0.40 (0.6)	0.90 (1.1)	0.38 (0.5)	0.84 (1.0)
11.	0.26 (0.6)	0.59 (0.9)	1.30 (1.6)	0.60 (0.8)	0.65 (0.9)	0.75 (0.9)
12.	0.55 (0.7)	0.83 (1.0)	0.72 (1.0)	0.66 (0.7)	1.00 (1.0)	0.68 (1.0)
13.	0.70 (0.9)	0.42 (0.6)	0.98 (1.3)	0.20 (0.4)	0.68 (1.0)	0.80 (1.0)
14.	0.37 (0.4)	0.67 (1.0)	0.40 (0.6)	0.74 (1.0)	0.43 (0.4)	0.91 (1.1)
15.	0.25 (0.4)	0.43 (0.6)	0.29 (0.6)	0.56 (0.9)	0.78 (1.2)	0.64 (1.0)
16.	0.72 (0.9)	0.47 (0.6)	0.48 (0.8)	0.56 (0.7)	0.69 (1.0)	0.40 (0.6)
17.	0.37 (0.8)		1.40 (1.6)	0.58 (0.7)	0.60 (0.8)	0.53 (0.7)
18.	0.43 (0.6)		1.27 (1.5)	0.35 (0.7)	0.61 (1.0)	0.66 (0.7)
19.	0.51 (0.9)			0.59 (0.9)	0.77 (1.4)	0.65 (1.0)
20.	0.38 (0.5)			0.75 (1.0)	0.91 (1.0)	1.60 (1.6)
21.	0.18 (0.4)			1.10 (1.2)	0.64 (1.1)	
22.	0.30 (0.4)			0.21 (0.4)	0.63 (0.8)	
23.	0.42 (0.8)			1.27 (1.4)	0.93 (1.1)	
24.	0.18 (0.5)			0.38 (0.6)		
25.	0.41 (0.5)			0.64 (0.7)		
26.	0.72 (1.1)			0.17 (0.4)		
27.	1.25 (1.6)			0.42 (0.5)		
28.	0.25 (0.5)			0.91 (1.2)		
29.	0.51 (0.7)			0.50 (0.9)		
30.	0.19 (0.4)			0.13 (0.3)		
31.	0.28 (0.5)			0.54 (0.7)		
32.	0.53 (0.6)			0.48 (0.7)		
33.				0.70 (0.8)		
34.				0.71 (0.9)		
35.				1.06 (1.1)		

T-6 contain largely non-coupled primary spans. In Kinetogram T-6, only the first primary span is coupled to the preceding span, which in this case is a secondary span. The *TAC* is 0.6, which shows a high degree of terminal coupling activity for the close-coupled element, *periodic chart, 11.*

To facilitate comparisons among the various transcripts, Table 4 displays the mean fundamental coefficients, the total mean progression density ($\bar{D}_S$) and new activity coefficient (*NAC*) for each transcript, and lists of mean progression densities and new activity coefficients for secondary spans. It is apparent that those communications with high mean fundamental coefficients tend to have low mean progression densities. The mean progression density expresses both the rate at which new verbal elements are introduced in a span and the amount of commonality conserved at each step. The new activity coefficient (cited in parentheses in the table) is the mean number of new elements introduced per discourse unit in the span. The lowest mean progression density is found in transcript T-2 ($\bar{D}_S = 0.38$), where, on the average, a new verbal element is introduced for every two discourse units (*NAC* = 0.6). Transcript T-6 presents the highest mean progression density ($\bar{D}_S = 0.75$), and here, new elements appear at the average rate of nearly one per discourse unit (*NAC* = 0.9). If the theoretical optimal mean progression density of 0.5, with *NAC* = 1.0, is accepted as a criterion, then transcript T-1 approaches the optimum quite closely.

The variation in organization of secondary spans can be ascertained by examining the Kinetograms and their summary tables. A common organizational scheme is prevalent in Kinetograms T-1, T-3, and T-5, where some of the secondary spans are initiated with a gain series and terminate with a decay series. Examples of this organizational pattern are cited in Table 5.

TABLE 5. SECONDARY SPANS CONTAINING A GAIN-DECAY SEQUENCE

Kinetogram	*Secondary Spans*
T-1	3, 5, 14, 26, 28
T-3	2, 8, 12
T-5	5, 10

The density (frequency) of pulses (Kinetogram spikes) varies among the communications. The lowest occurs in transcript T-1 and the highest in T-6 (Kinetograms are in Appendices B and G). The mean pulse density, the number of pulses of all kinds in a Kinetogram divided by the number of discourse units, is shown for all six transcripts in Table 6.

TABLE 6. MEAN PULSE DENSITY IN SIX TRANSCRIPTS

Transcript	*Mean Pulse Density*
T-1	0.29
T-2	0.30
T-3	0.31
T-4	0.29
T-5	0.30
T-6	0.32

The reality and artificiality of pulses can be determined by comparing the variation in B_2 values composing the pulse with the corresponding B_1 values. If the B_1 values follow the same trend as the B_2 values, then the pulse is real. A real pulse occurs when a speaker introduces an idea and follows through on it in successive statements. The B_1 and corresponding B_2 values trend downward with the appearance of the new idea and upward with the follow-through, and a spike is produced on the Kinetogram. An artificial pulse occurs when a speaker fails to follow through with a new idea and introduces different and much less potent ideas. The B_2 values increase, producing a Kinetogram spike, whereas the corresponding B_1 values decrease or remain constant. The pulse is artificial, because the spike is produced by a decrease in potency rather than an increase in commonality. The percentages of artificial pulses in the six transcripts are, in consecutive order: 22, 23, 17, 21, 25, and 30 per cent. Some artificial pulses in Kinetogram T-1 occur at the following discourse units: 21–22, 31–33, 36–38, 59–60, 109–110, and 122–123. Examples of real pulses occur at discourse units 34–35, 64–65, 130–131, 132–133, 227–229, and 250–251. The reader can confirm these by comparing the B_1 values in Appendix B with the B_2 plots of Kinetogram T-1. A pulse is considered real if 50 per cent or more of the B_1 values follow the same trend as the B_2 values.

The distribution of fundamental coefficients of structure follows a consistent pattern among the six transcripts. A large percentage of coefficients occur in the interval $B_1 = 0.0–0.1$ and again in the intervals $B_1 = 0.5–0.6$ and $B_1 = 0.6–0.7$. Transcript T-3 is unique in containing 9.9 per cent of all B_1 coefficients in the interval

$B_1 = 0.2–0.3$. The remaining transcripts have only 5 per cent or lower occurrence in this same interval. All of these data support the generalization that classroom science communications are so organized that a majority of fundamental coefficients occur at or near the levels of $B_1 = 0.0$ and $B_1 = 0.5$. The generality of this principle among different science lessons and in other disciplines will require more extensive observations.

Variations in theme activity occur both within and among the transcripts. Scatter diagrams for all six transcripts clearly show positive correlations between theme activity within secondary spans and their mean fundamental coefficients of structure. To illustrate this phenomenon as well as the divergencies from it, Table 7 shows the various combinations of theme activity and mean fundamental coefficients for some secondary spans in transcript T-1. The secondary spans are identified by their discourse units. The distinctive quality of the discourse contained in each span may be ascertained by examining the transcript (Appendix B).

TABLE 7. THEME ACTIVITY AND KINETIC STRUCTURE IN SELECTED SPANS OF DISCOURSE IN T-1

Theme Activity \ Kinetic Structure ($\overline{B}_1$)	High	Low
High	D.U. 114-121 D.U. 187-193	D.U. 165-173 D.U. 250-256
Low	D.U. 1-5 D.U. 68-76	D.U. 47-60 D.U. 122-131

The total amount of theme activity varies among the transcripts. Table 8 contains a summary of the percentage of secondary spans in each communication containing a dominant verbal element with

TABLE 8. PERCENTAGES OF SECONDARY SPANS WITH RAC OF 0.50 OR GREATER IN TRANSCRIPTS T-1 THROUGH T-6

Transcript	*Percentage*
T-1	63
T-2	81
T-3	61
T-4	66
T-5	65
T-6	40

$RAC = 0.5$ or greater. The higher the *RAC* value, the greater is the theme activity.

A convenient quantitative estimate of static structure is the mean B_2 value of a span. The lower the $\bar{B}_2$ value, the higher the probability that the span contains static structures. Since B_2 values are computed on the basis of the total activity (Σf) in each communication, and since this is a variable between communications, each B_2 value should be converted to a standard form before precise statements comparing spans in different lessons can be rendered. To accomplish this, all B_2 values are converted (using Figure 13, Chapter II) to a standard form based on the common factor $\Sigma f = 500$. The B_2 value to be converted is located on the ordinate. Its corresponding B_1 value is located on the abscissa bearing the appropriate Σf for the communication under analysis. The intercept of these two coordinates defines the diagonal guideline representing $(F' + F'')$ to be used in performing the conversion. Now, the B_1 value is relocated on the abscissa marked $\Sigma f = 500$ and the diagonal guideline identified in the previous step is used to locate the new B_2 value on the ordinate. The mean B_2 value is then computed for the entire span and the comparisons among communications are performed.

As an example, suppose a B_2 value of 0.8, corresponding to a B_1 of 0.5 and obtained from a communication with $\Sigma f = 300$, is to be converted to the standard form based on $\Sigma f = 500$. The B_2 and B_1 coordinates intersect with the diagonal line labeled 50. Now, the coordinate $B_1 = 0.5$ is relocated on the abscissa labeled $\Sigma f = 500$, and, using the same diagonal line (labeled 50) as a guide, the approximately correct new B_2 value is obtained on the ordinate; thus, $B_2 = 0.84$.

Comparisons between Kinetogram spans using converted B_2 values allow one to determine the relative potency of the verbal elements in the spans being compared. The constant value for the total activity, $\Sigma f = 500$, removes one source of variation in the potency factor and hence the determining quantity is the partial activity terms $(F' + F'')$. As an example of a comparison of weighted coefficients for Kinetogram spans in two lessons, the secondary span D.U. 94–104 ($\bar{B}_2 = 0.87$) in T-1 will be compared to a similar static-structured sequence, D.U. 49–65 ($\bar{B}_2 = 0.80$), in T-2. When the mean weighted coefficients are converted to the standard form, the differences between the two become less salient; thus, $\bar{B}_2$ for the T-1 span becomes 0.85 and $\bar{B}_2$ for the T-2 span becomes 0.82. There is less difference in potency between the elements of the two spans than is apparent from observation of the Kinetogram summary table containing non-converted $\bar{B}_2$ values. When making comparisons among Kinetograms based on internal relations within or among secondary spans, it obviously is not necessary to convert the B_2 values to the standard form.

In the secondary spans of transcripts T-1 through T-6, mean weighted coefficients of structure ($\bar{B}_2$) and mean progression densities ($\bar{D}_S$) are in large measure inversely related to one another. As explained in Chapter I, kinetic structure tends to be inversely related to progression density. In a Kinetogram, high kinetic structure usually appears as a span wherein the Kinetogram trace is clearly elevated in relation to the position of the spikes in the total graph. For example, in Kinetogram T-1 (in Appendix B) secondary spans 7, 15, 17, and 30, to cite a few, clearly contain an elevated central trace. In these spans the kinetic structure is high and static structure is low. Conversely, in the same Kinetogram, secondary spans 8, 10, 16, and 21 have depressed traces whose mean B_2 values are below the mean for the total communication. In these spans static structure is high and progression density is high. That is, the mean progression density for these spans is higher than the grand mean for all secondary spans in the whole communication.

In general, when a Kinetogram trace in a secondary span is clearly elevated above the level of the mean in the whole Kinetogram, the mean progression density in that span will be lower than the total mean progression density for the whole communication. (In all cases reported here, total mean progression density for a whole communication will mean the grand mean of its secondary span means.) When, however, the Kinetogram trace in a secondary span is clearly depressed below the mean level for the total Kinetogram, the mean progression density in that span will tend to be higher than the total mean progression density for the whole communication. Stated another way, secondary spans with high kinetic structure, as determined by the trace in a Kinetogram, will have a lower rate of new information presentation than those secondary spans dominated by low kinetic structure, where the Kinetogram trace is clearly depressed below the mean level.

The Kinetogram trace, then, can be used to make estimates about the degree of commonality (kinetic structure) in a span and also the amount of progression density contained therein. Exceptions to this rule are encountered. For example, in Kinetogram T-5 (in Appendix F) secondary span 13 has a clearly elevated trace. However, the progression density is higher than the mean value for the total communication by a small amount (+0.003). Since this is such a small positive deviation from the total $\bar{D}_S$ it is clearly not a significant exception to the rule. This secondary span, moreover, is interesting because it illustrates how such exceptions arise. The progression density is enhanced because the teacher introduces several low-activity terms in the discussion of molluscs. Since these are low-activity elements and much of the surrounding discourse in the span is highly integrated, the Kinetogram trace is not depressed. The mean fundamental coefficient for this span is equal to the mean value for the total communication. When such small differences are encountered, it is likely that the rule of inverse relation between progression density and commonality (kinetic structure) will not hold. This is why it is very useful to correlate B_1 values with the Kinetogram trace when performing analyses. If one observes that the $\bar{B}_1$ value for a span deviates only slightly from the mean for the whole communication, then it is probable that no precise prediction can be made relating kinetic structure to progression density in that span.

The discourse contained in secondary span 13 is presented here to allow the reader to note how the rapid rate of information progression in the middle part (D.U. 132 and 133) enhances the mean progression density in the total span.

129.	No, sea urchin comes under here, under the molluscs.	83, 77
----	Barnacles?	
130.	Barnacles come under here.	84
131.	No, barnacles come under here (molluscs).	84, 77
132.	All right, under the molluscs—an example of this, these are soft-bodied creatures, such as the squid and octopus, which may or may not have a shell.	77, 85, 86, 87, 88
----	Molluscs?	

133. Yes, a mollusc, and when it does have a shell, it would be one like an oyster or a clam.	77, 88, 89, 76
134. Its body is essentially soft.	77, 85
135. There is no bone in it.	77, 90
136. So clams, oysters, octopuses would be examples of a mollusc.	76, 89, 87, 77

In general, this segment of discourse is highly structured, contains a consistent theme (*mollusc, 77*) and, as observed, produces an elevated trace in the Kinetogram. It is the massive thrust of low-activity verbal elements in D.U. 132 and 133 which produces such an uncommonly high progression density for the whole span.

TABLE 9. SECONDARY SPANS IN KINETOGRAMS T-1 THROUGH T-6 ILLUSTRATING AN INVERSE RELATION BETWEEN KINETIC STRUCTURE AND MEAN PROGRESSION DENSITY

Kinetogram	*High Kinetic Structure Low Progression Density*	*Low Kinetic Structure High Progression Density*
T-1	7, 15, 17, 23, 24, 28, 30	8, 10, 12, 13, 16, 27
T-2	2, 4, 7, 9	8, 14, 16
T-3	2, 5, 8, 16	11, 13, 17, 18
T-4	2, 4, 13, 16, 18, 19, 22, 26, 27, 29, 30	1, 5, 7, 9, 23, 28
T-5	4, 5, 10, 14, 17, 18	6, 7, 9, 12
T-6	3, 7, 16	4, 5, 10, 13

There are many examples of Kinetogram spans which do follow the inverse law between commonality and progression density in secondary spans. Table 9 identifies some secondary spans in transcripts T-1 through T-6 wherein the inverse relation holds. In this table, the headings *High Kinetic Structure* and *Low Kinetic Structure* mean respectively those spans whose mean B_2 coefficients were greater or less than the mean value in the whole communication. The same explanation holds true for the headings *High Progression Density* and *Low Progression Density*. The reader should carefully examine the Kinetogram traces corresponding to the secondary spans listed, to become familiar with their organization. The mean progression densities listed in Table 4 should also be reviewed, to sharpen perception of the inverse relation between the Kinetogram traces and the mean progression densities. It is advisable to make thorough use of transcript T-1, presented in Appendix B, to develop a knowledge of the meaning of progression density and of various levels of B_2 values as they appear in various secondary spans. When such knowledge has been mastered, the Kinetogram traces and their correlated secondary span characteristics will be more meaningful, thereby allowing more information retrieval from analysis of the Kinetograms alone.

In over-all perspective, transcript T-6 (a chemistry lesson) is clearly different from the remaining ones, whose content is largely biological. Transcript T-6 has the lowest theme activity, the highest pulse density, and one of the highest total mean progression densities among all of the communications examined. In short, it is the least kinetic-structured and progresses at the most rapid rate. The activity histogram of Figure 17 illustrates the recurrent and alternating activity of two dominant elements in transcript T-6—activity which contributes to the extended series of pulses and static structures dominating the communication. Transcript T-2 is organizationally diametrically opposed to T-6. The mean fundamental coefficient is highest ($\bar{B}_1 = 0.44$) among all of the communications studied, the theme activity is highest, and the mean progression density and mean pulse density are among the lowest observed. It is therefore more structured than T-6; it presents discrete secondary spans with clearly discernible themes or integrating ideas and progresses at a lower rate than found in T-6.

In general, the communications analyzed here form a spectrum beginning with higher-structured ones at the beginning (T-1 and T-2) and progressing toward lower-structured ones (T-5 and T-6) at the end.

Finally, the quantitative methods of analysis described here provide a reliable and systematic method for the identification and structural classification of discourse spans in a communication. They should be applicable to interaction analysis of discourse among several speakers as well as to the monologue analyses performed here. In such cases, the degree of commonality between successive statements by different speakers would be determined and the quantitative procedures presented here for the analysis of monologues would be applied to the total sequence of interaction discourse units.

References

1. Anderson, O. R. "The Application of Psychological Theory to the Analysis of Structure in Science Teaching." *Science Education* 53, 227–30; 1969.
2. Anderson, O. R. "An Interdisciplinary Theory of Behavior." *Journal of Research in Science Teaching* 6, 265–73; 1969.
3. Anderson, O. R. *Structure in Teaching: Theory and Analysis.* New York: Teachers College Press, 1969.
4. Bard, P. "Receptor Organs and Discharges in Sensory Nerves." *Medical Physiology.* St. Louis: C. V. Mosby Co., 1956.
5. Barrington, E. J. W. *Invertebrate Structure and Function.* Boston: Houghton Mifflin Co., 1968.
6. Bridges, C. D. B. "The Visual Pigments of the Rainbow Trout (*Salmo irideus*)." *Journal of Physiology* 134, 620–29; 1956.
7. Bridges, C. D. B. "Visual Pigments of Some Common Laboratory Mammals." *Nature* 184, 1727–28; 1959.
8. Bruner, J. S. "The Course of Cognitive Growth." *American Psychologist* 19, 1–15; 1964.
9. Bunning, E., & Schneiderhohn, G. "Uber das Aktionsspektrum der phototaktischen Reaktionen von Euglena." *Archiv für Mikrobiologie* 24, 80–90; 1956.
10. Carter, G. S. *General Zoology of the Invertebrates.* London: Sidgwick and Jackson, 1961.
11. Collins, F. D., & Morton, R. A. "Studies on Rhodopsin. I: Methods of Extraction and the Absorption Spectrum." *Biochemical Journal* 47, 3–10; 1950.

12. Crescitelli, F., & Dartnall, H. J. A. "Human Visual Purple." *Nature* 172, 195–97; 1953.

13. De Soto, C. B.; London, M.; & Handel, S. "Social Reasoning and Spatial Paralogic." *Journal of Personality and Social Psychology* 2, 513–21; 1965.

14. Dogiel, V. A. *General Protozoology* (Revised by Poljanskij, J. I., & Chejsin, E. M.). Oxford: Oxford University Press, 1965.

15. Hartline, H. K.; Wagner, H. G.; & MacNichol, E. F., Jr. "The Peripheral Origin of Nervous Activity in the Visual System." *Cold Spring Harbor Symposia on Quantitative Biology* 17, 125–41; 1952.

16. Hubbard, R., & St. George, R. C. C. "The Rhodopsin System of the Squid." *Journal of General Physiology* 41, 501–28; 1958.

17. Hubbard, R., & Wald, G. "Visual Pigment of the Horseshoe Crab, *Limulus polyphemus*." *Nature* 186, 212–15; 1960.

18. James, T. W. *Synchrony in Cell Division and Growth* (Edited by Zeuthen, E.). New York: Interscience, 1964.

19. Kavanau, J. L. "Some Physico-chemical Aspects of Life and Evolution in Relation to the Living State." *American Naturalist* 81, 161–84; 1947.

20. Klein, B. "Das Silberlinien- oder Neuroformative System der Ciliaten." *Annalen Naturhistorisches Museum Wien* 53, 156–336; 1943.

21. Leedale, G. F. "Periodicity of Mitosis and Cell Division in the Euglenineae." *Biological Bulletin* 116, 162–74; 1959.

22. Milne, L. J., & Milne, M. "Photosensitivity in Invertebrates." *Handbook of Physiology*, Vol. 1, Sec. 1. Washington: American Physiological Society, 1959.

23. Olson, D. R., & Baker, N. E. "Children's Recall of Spatial Orientation of Objects." *The Journal of Genetic Psychology* 114, 273–81; 1969.

24. Peskin, J. C. "Photolabile Pigments in Invertebrates." *Science* 114, 120–21; 1951.

25. Prosser, C. L., & Brown, F. A., Jr. *Comparative Animal Physiology.* Philadelphia: W. B. Saunders Co., 1961.

26. Ranson, S. W. *Anatomy of the Nervous System* (Revised by Clark, S. L.). Philadelphia: W. B. Saunders Co., 1959.

27. Robinson, C. E. "A Chemical Model of Long-term Memory and Recall." *Molecular Basis of Some Aspects of Mental Activity* (Edited by Walaas, O.). New York: Academic Press, 1966.

28. Seaman, G. "Localization of Acetylcholinesterase Activity in the Protozoan *Tetrahymena geleii S.*" *Proceedings of the Society for Experimental Biology and Medicine* 76, 169–70; 1951.

29. Snedecor, G. W., & Cochran, W. G. *Statistical Methods.* Ames: Iowa State University Press, 1962.

30. Wald, G. "The Photoreceptor Function of the Carotenoids and Vitamins A." *Vitamins and Hormones* (Edited by Harris, R. S., & Thimann, K. V.), Vol. 1. New York: Academic Press, 1943.

31. Wald, G. "The Photoreceptor Process in Vision." *Handbook of Physiology*, Vol. 1, Sec. 1. Washington: American Physiological Society, 1959.

32. Wald, G. "Visual Pigments and Vitamins A of the Clawed Toad, *Xenopus laevis.*" *Nature* 175, 390–91; 1955.

33. Wald, G.; Brown, P. K.; & Kennedy, D. "The Visual System of the Alligator." *Journal of General Physiology* 40, 703–14; 1957.

34. Wald, G.; Brown, P. K.; & Smith, P. H. "Iodopsin." *Journal of General Physiology* 38, 623–81; 1955.

35. Wald, G., & Burg, S. P. "The Vitamin A of the Lobster." *Journal of General Physiology* 40, 909–26; 1957.

APPENDIX A

Transcript T-A and Related Materials

Transcript T-A

1.	Quills on a porcupine, these are a kind of special adaptation of hairs.	1, 2, 3, 4
2.	Another thing would be the kind of horny structure on rhinoceros.	5, 6, 7
3.	This is also something that has the same kind of development from hair-like roots; that hair does in other organisms.	5, 6, 8, 9, 4, 11
4.	All right, any other characteristics?	12
----	They have, uhh, their young are born alive and they give birth.	
5.	OK, one thing that they (mammals) all do is feed their young milk.	13, 14, 15, 16
----	And they're born alive, OK? They're not an egg.	
6.	And practically all of them except for a few strange characters are born alive, yes.	13, 17, 18
7.	So it indicates that it is live-bearing.	17, 18, 19
8.	Which means that the adult mammals bear their young alive.	13, 15, 18, 20, 21
9.	What is the name of the one that doesn't?	13, 22
10.	It does lay eggs.	13, 23, 24
11.	One of the mammals.	13
----	Platypus?	
12.	Yes, the platypus.	25
13.	What is another example of one that lays eggs?	13, 23, 24
----	Does a whale lay eggs?	
----	Turtles, turtles lay eggs.	
----	Turtles are reptiles.	
14.	OK, another characteristic here is the fact that all of these animals are warm-blooded.	12, 26, 27
15.	You might put an asterisk before both of these, because these are characteristics of mammals only.	12, 13

16.	Now down here, the fact that they are warm-blooded is something that they share in common with birds.	13, 27, 28
17.	So that doesn't really distinguish the mammals, but it is an important thing—all mammals are warm-blooded.	13, 27, 29
18.	There are not any that are cold-blooded.	13, 30
----	What difference is there between warm-blooded and cold-blooded?	
19.	Can anyone tell us what the differences are?	31
----	I think because the warm-blooded, you get your warmth.	
----	The warm-blooded animal, he has a set body temperature and if you take a cold-blooded animal such as a fish, if the temperature outside gets colder, they get colder; and if it gets hotter, they get hotter.	
20.	Yes, right, so if they're warm-blooded, they have mechanisms for regulating body temperature.	13, 27, 32, 33, 34
21.	For instance in human beings, in human beings the body temperature is maintained at 98 degrees no matter whether it is minus 20 degrees outside or 120 degrees.	34, 35, 36, 37
----	[Long rambling student statement]	
22.	Then they defrost it?	38
23.	Warm-blooded, I was just explaining that.	27
24.	Something that goes along with, not really but in addition to, their being warm-blooded is the fact that they have a heart with four chambers in it.	13, 27, 39, 40
25.	What would the names of these four chambers be?	40
----	Auricle and ventricle.	
26.	Left and right [auricles] or left and right ventricles—we went through all of that early in the year.	41, 42
27.	And what goes along with this four-chambered heart is the fact that part of the heart is sending blood over to the lungs to receive oxygen and to get rid of carbon dioxide.	39, 40, 43, 44, 45, 46
28.	The other part of the heart is sending blood out to all parts of the body.	39, 43, 47, 48
29.	So there are really two places to which blood is being sent.	43

30.	And this has to do with the fact that we breathe using—	49
----	Lungs.	
31.	Lungs, part of the blood is sent from the left part of the heart over to the lungs.	39, 43, 44
32.	Other parts of the blood are sent throughout the body.	43, 47, 48
----	Are these characteristics for mammals?	
33.	No, because these are characteristics that the birds share also.	12, 28, 43, 47, 48
34.	Only the first two are very specific to the mammals.	13, 14, 15, 16, 17, 18
----	Birds have two sides [to the heart]?	
35.	They are able to lower body temperature below 98.6, but I'm not sure how much success they have with it.	34, 50
----	The fish when they freeze, does their body just stop working?	
36.	Apparently so, everything just slows down very, very much.	51
37.	I don't know how long they can keep them frozen.	52, 53
38.	Do you have any idea how long they can keep these fish frozen?	52, 53
39.	The heart chambers—ventricles, the lower ones, and auricles, the upper ones.	10, 54, 55
40.	Let's do the birds since they have more characteristics in common with the mammals.	12, 13, 28
41.	All right, the birds, what is one thing characteristic about the birds?	12, 28
----	When they feed their young, they chew the food and, uh, spit it up and feed the young.	
42.	Do all birds feed their young that way?	14, 15, 28
43.	We're trying to think of all the things that living things called birds would share in common.	28
----	They have feathers.	
44.	Right, they have feathers.	28, 56
45.	Instead of hair or fur, they have feathers.	4, 28, 56, 57
----	They also have two stomachs; one that helps them	

	digest food where they swallow rocks and—well, most of them do.	
46.	Most of them do.	28, 56
47.	What is something else that all of them share?	28
----	Penguins have hair.	
48.	Well, I have never seen a penguin up close.	58
49.	What else is there that would make a penguin birds and not a mammal?	13, 28, 58
----	Two feet.	
50.	Two feet?	59
51.	All of the birds have wings.	28, 60
52.	You might find an occasional one here or there that when it gets to be an adult doesn't look as though it has wings, because the wings haven't developed very much and there are a few that can't fly.	8, 20, 28, 60, 61
53	And there may be the confusion also going back to the mammals something like the bat.	13, 62
54.	It does have wings.	60, 62
55.	Or it does have structures for flying.	61, 62
----	It shouldn't be considered wings.	
56.	But since it has hair and it has these other characteristics, it goes with mammals.	4, 12, 13
----	We were at camp and we went in this mine and up on the walls are little bitty bats; you know, they hang all over the walls.	
57.	The next time you go there how about getting some?	62
----	Don't they bite?	
----	Penguin body	
58.	You have a picture of a penguin in your book.	58, 63
59.	In addition to these two distinct characteristics, there are a few other things that they share in common with the mammals.	12, 13, 28
----	Well, if they're warm-blooded, they'll have lungs.	
60.	If they are warm-blooded, if you dissect them, you would find lungs, or, if you observed them alive, you would find that they breathe.	18, 27, 44 49, 64
61.	How do you migrate down to South America?	65, 66
----	You can fly down in an airplane.	

62.	The fact that they are warm-blooded doesn't have too much to do with that.	27, 28
63.	They can maintain constant body temperature.	28, 34, 67
64.	Now animals that are not able to maintain a constant body temperature may go through some difficulties.	26, 67
----	What about the feet?	
65.	Yes, the feet and the beaks.	59, 68
66.	The feet and also the beaks on birds we might say have a great number of adaptations.	3, 28, 59, 68
----	What about flying fish?	
67.	Various adaptations for the kinds of life they live—beaks obviously for the kind of food they eat.	3, 69, 68, 70, 71
68.	Are they eating something soft or are they eating something hard that they have to crack?	28, 71, 72, 73, 74
69.	With the feet, what kind of land or structure do they usually stand on?	6, 59, 75
70.	Are they usually up on a limb which will allow them to have feet which will grasp the limb?	59, 76, 77
71.	Do they swim where the webbed foot would be the most likely kind of adaptation?	3, 78, 79
----	Amphibians or reptiles have those too.	
72.	The point here is that there are a lot of adaptations.	3
----	Do birds have scales on their feet?	
73.	Yeah, you could add that to the ones right there.	59, 80
74.	Along their feet and legs they do have very scaly structures.	6, 59, 80, 81
----	Do penguins lay eggs?	
75.	Yes, penguins lay eggs.	23, 24, 58
----	What do the reptiles?	
76.	Basically, what are the characteristics of the reptiles?	12, 82
----	They're cold-blooded.	
77.	They're cold-blooded.	30, 82
78.	Now that's not a specific thing for reptiles, for they share that in common with a number of other classes.	82, 83
----	On their bodies, they have scales.	
79.	Yes, on their bodies they have scales.	48, 80

80.	This is something that separates them from the amphibians.	82, 84, 85
81.	As you look at this tomorrow, well, I guess you won't have a chance to look at the chameleons, I guess they're not there.	86
82.	In the back you can observe those and also these, lizard and a salamander.	87, 88
83.	The lizard and the salamander look very much alike.	87, 88
84.	But the big difference between them, the lizard being a reptile, the salamander being an amphibian, is the fact that the reptiles have scales on their body.	31, 48, 80, 82, 84, 87, 88
85.	And they usually can go into much drier places.	82, 89
86.	The moisture doesn't evaporate as quickly from their body.	48, 90, 91
----	A lot of reptiles shed their skin.	
87.	A lot of reptiles do shed their skin, yes.	82, 92, 93
88.	They don't all.	82
----	Is the armadillo a reptile?	
----	They're cold-blooded.	
89.	All right, let's put that down.	30, 82
----	Is the armadillo a reptile or a mammal?	
90.	That's what you have to do, you have to check which of the characteristics they have.	12, 82
91.	Find out as many characteristics of it as you can so you can find out what it is.	12
92.	All right, cold-blooded; what else, what are the other characteristics here?	12, 30
93.	They lay eggs.	23, 82
94.	How does it breathe?	49, 82
95.	How do reptiles breathe?	49, 82
96.	Do they have gills or do they have lungs?	44, 82, 94
----	They have gills.	
----	They have lungs. (chorus of voices)	
97.	Yes, if you dissect a reptile, a snake or a turtle, a lizard, you would find that there are lungs inside.	44, 64, 82, 88, 95, 96, 97
98.	Finally, there is a difference between the reptiles as compared to the birds and the mammals.	13, 31, 28, 82

99.	The heart is a little bit different.	31, 39
100.	It has three chambers.	39, 98
----	It has a three-chambered heart.	
101.	Three-chambered heart, it doesn't have the four.	40, 82, 98
----	What does the three-chambered heart do?	
102.	It pumps blood.	43, 98, 99
103.	We don't have as much of a separation of the blood.	43, 85
104.	In the four-chambered heart we have half of the heart receiving blood coming back from the body.	39, 40, 43, 48
105.	The left hand side is picking up blood from the lungs and receiving it back.	43, 44, 100
106.	So you have a separation of blood coming back from the body and immediately receiving oxygen.	43, 48, 45
----	You have blood on each side.	
107.	Yes, there's a difference in the amount of oxygen.	31, 45
108.	Now when you have the three-chambered heart, you you don't have as much of the blood.	39, 45, 98
----	Do the reptiles kill themselves, like a snake will kill a turtle?	
109.	Do you mean do some reptiles feed on others as prey?	14, 82, 101
110.	Next class will be the amphibians.	83, 84
111.	In order to compare these with the amphibians—in order to compare reptiles with amphibians.	82, 84
112.	They lack scales.	80, 84, 102
113.	So if you have two creatures such as lizard, salamander that look very much alike, see which one has scales, it goes to the reptiles, the other one goes to the amphibians.	80, 82, 84, 87, 88, 103
----	They have gills.	
----	They don't have scales.	
114.	Right, they don't have scales.	80, 84
115.	At some point in their life they usually have gills and at another point they have lungs.	44, 69, 84, 94
116.	This is where your term amphibian comes from because part of their life is spent in the water where the gills are used.	69, 84, 94, 104
117.	And then another part on land where the lungs are used.	44, 69, 105

Kinetogram Summary Table for Transcript T-A

Mean Fundamental Coefficient	Mean Weighted Coefficient
0.29	0.83
Total Number of Discourse Units	Verbal Elements Total Frequency
117	319
Number of Primary Spans	Primary Span Mean Length
3	32
Number of Secondary Spans	Secondary Span Mean Length
16	7

	Origin	*Conclusion*	$\bar{B}_1$	$\bar{B}_2$	*Verbal Elements*	*Transition*	*TAC*
Primary Span							
1	5	33	0.23	0.83	Mammal, 13		
2	40	75	0.25	0.83	Birds, 28	NC	–
3	76	109	0.34	0.84	Reptiles, 82	C-3	0.75
Secondary Span							
1	1	4	0.11	0.64	Horny, 5 Structure, 6		
2	5	13	0.27	0.84	Mammal, 13	NC	–
3	14	19	0.31	0.81	Warm-blooded, 27	C-3	0.18
4	20	23	0.06	0.81	Body temperature, 34	C-2	0.40
5	24	33	0.27	0.85	Heart, 39 Blood, 43	C-2	0.67
6	34	39	0.17	0.84	Frozen, 52 Fish, 53	NC	–
7	40	52	0.42	0.87	Characteristics, 12	NC	–
8	53	59	0.14	0.78	Bat, 62	C-3	1.00
9	60	64	0.16	0.80	Warm-blooded, 27	NC	–
10	65	75	0.26	0.85	Feet, 59	NC	–
11	76	81	0.17	0.78	Reptiles, 82	NC	–
12	82	86	0.33	0.86	Lizard, 88	NC	–
13	87	92	0.49	0.90	Reptiles, 82	NC	–
14	93	97	0.46	0.88	Lungs, 44 Breathe, 49	NC	–
15	98	109	0.30	0.83	Heart, 39	C-2	0.25
16	110	117	0.40	0.85	Amphibians, 84	C-3	0.40
Gain Series:							
Artificial pulsed	60	66	0.21	0.82			
Artificial linear	34	38	0.20	0.83			
	80	83	0.25	0.83			

(Continued overleaf)

Kinetogram Summary Table for Transcript T-A (Continued)

	Origin	Conclusion	$\bar{B}_1$	$\bar{B}_2$
Decay Series:				
Real linear	67	69	0.22	0.78
Symmetries:				
Real, two-point	12	13	0.00	0.74
	19	20	0.00	0.72
	30	31	0.00	0.79
	45	46	0.67	0.96
	56	57	0.00	0.73
	79	80	0.00	0.70
	86	87	0.00	0.70
	107	108	0.4	0.88

DISTRIBUTION OF FUNDAMENTAL COEFFICIENTS

Interval	Percentage of Coefficients Occurring in Each Interval
0.000–0.095	40.17
0.096–0.195	0.85
0.196–0.295	6.83
0.296–0.395	5.12
0.396–0.495	18.80
0.496–0.595	12.82
0.596–0.695	9.40
0.696–0.795	1.70
0.796–0.895	0.85
0.896–1.000	2.56

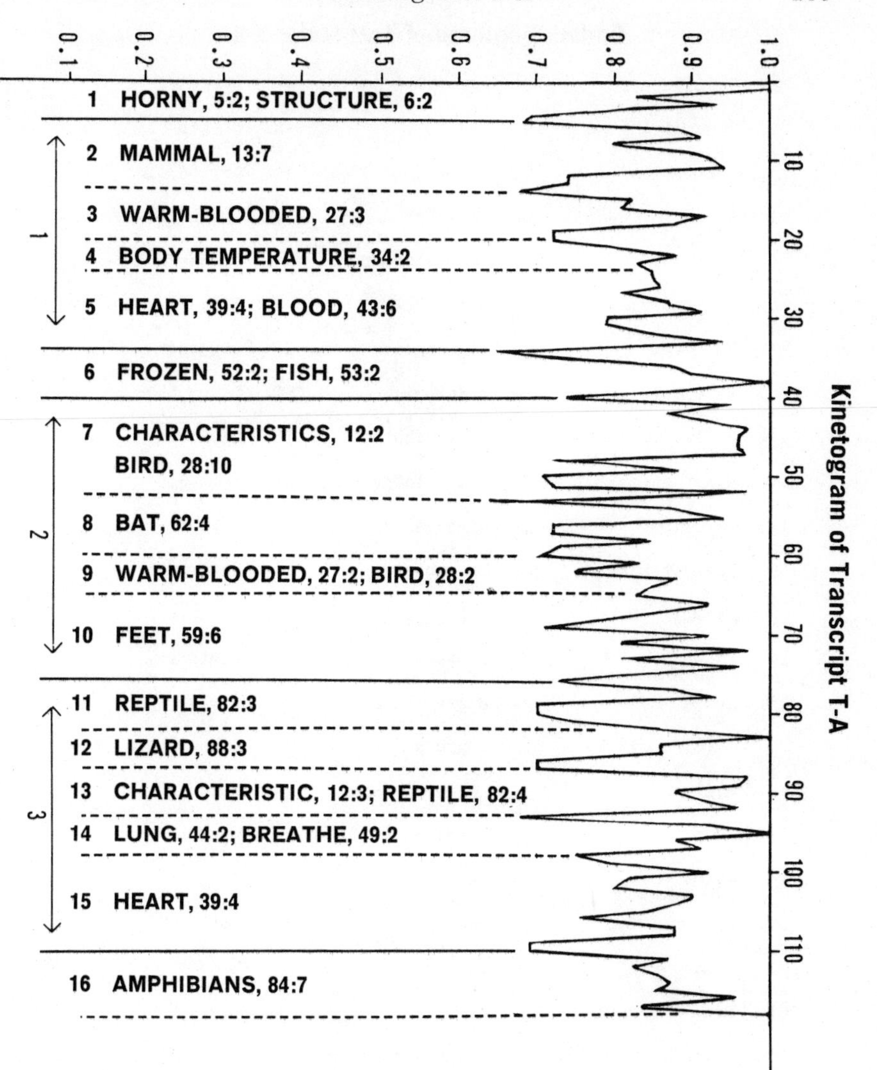
0.1
0.2
0.3
0.4
0.5
0.6
0.7
0.8
0.9
1.0
1 HORNY, 5:2; STRUCTURE, 6:2
2 MAMMAL, 13:7
3 WARM-BLOODED, 27:3
4 BODY TEMPERATURE, 34:2
5 HEART, 39:4; BLOOD, 43:6
6 FROZEN, 52:2; FISH, 53:2
7 CHARACTERISTICS, 12:2
BIRD, 28:10
8 BAT, 62:4
9 WARM-BLOODED, 27:2; BIRD, 28:2
10 FEET, 59:6
11 REPTILE, 82:3
12 LIZARD, 88:3
13 CHARACTERISTIC, 12:3; REPTILE, 82:4
14 LUNG, 44:2; BREATHE, 49:2
15 HEART, 39:4
16 AMPHIBIANS, 84:7
1
2
3
10
20
30
40
50
60
70
80
90
100
110
Kinetogram of Transcript T-A

Coded Elements of Transcript T-A

1. Quills
2. Porcupine
3. Adaptation
4. Hairs
5. Horny
6. Structure
7. Rhinoceros
8. Development
9. Hair-like roots
10. Heart chamber
11. Organism
12. Characteristics
13. Mammal
14. Feed
15. Young (offspring)
16. Milk
17. Born
18. Alive
19. Live-bearing
20. Adult
21. Bear (to carry young)
22. Name
23. Lay (to deposit)
24. Eggs
25. Platypus
26. Animals
27. Warm-blooded
28. Birds
29. Distinguish (a unique attribute)
30. Cold-blooded
31. Differences
32. Mechanisms
33. Regulating
34. Body temperature
35. Human beings
36. Degrees (temperature scale)
37. Outside
38. Defrost
39. Heart
40. Four-chambered
41. Left Ventricle
42. Right Ventricle
43. Blood
44. Lungs
45. Oxygen
46. Carbon dioxide
47. Part (Portion of body)
48. Body
49. Breathe
50. Lower (reduce)
51. Slowdown
52. Frozen
53. Fish
54. Ventricles
55. Auricles
56. Feathers
57. Fur
58. Penguin
59. Feet
60. Wings
61. Fly
62. Bat
63. Book
64. Dissect
65. Migrate
66. South America

67. Constant
68. Beaks
69. Life
70. Food
71. Eat
72. Soft
73. Hard
74. Crack
75. Stand
76. Limb
77. Grasp
78. Swim
79. Webbed foot
80. Scales, Scaly
81. Legs
82. Reptiles
83. Classes (taxonomic)
84. Amphibians
85. Separate (divide from)
86. Chameleons
87. Salamander
88. Lizard
89. Dry (arid)
90. Moisture
91. Evaporate
92. Shed
93. Skin
94. Gill
95. Snake
96. Turtle
97. Inside
98. Three-chambered
99. Pump
100. Left-hand side
101. Prey
102. Lack (be deficient)
103. Creatures
104. Water
105. Land

Code Summary Sheet for Transcript T-A

1)	1	2	3	4	0	0	0		
2)	5	6	7	0	0	0	0	Horny, 5	
3)	5	6	8	9	4	11	0	Structure,6	
4)	12	0	0	0	0	0	0		
5)	13	14	15	16	0	0	0		Mammal, 13
6)	13	17	18	0	0	0	0		
7)	17	18	19	0	0	0	0		
8)	13	20	21	15	18	0	0		
9)	22	13	0	0	0	0	0	Mammal, 13	
10)	13	23	24	0	0	0	0		
11)	13	0	0	0	0	0	0		
12)	25	0	0	0	0	0	0		
13)	13	23	24	0	0	0	0		
14)	12	26	27	0	0	0	0		
15)	12	13	0	0	0	0	0		
16)	27	13	28	0	0	0	0	Warm-	
17)	27	13	29	0	0	0	0	blooded, 27	
18)	13	30	0	0	0	0	0		
19)	31	0	0	0	0	0	0		
20)	27	13	32	33	34	0	0		
21)	35	34	36	37	0	0	0	Body	
22)	38	0	0	0	0	0	0	temperature, 34	
23)	27	0	0	0	0	0	0		
24)	13	27	39	40	0	0	0	Heart, 39	
25)	40	0	0	0	0	0	0	Blood, 43	
26)	41	42	0	0	0	0	0		

27)	39	40	43	44	45	46	0	
28)	47	39	43	48	0	0	0	
29)	43	0	0	0	0	0	0	
30)	49	0	0	0	0	0	0	
31)	44	43	39	0	0	0	0	
32)	47	43	48	0	0	0	0	
33)	47	43	48	12	28	0	0	
34)	13	14	15	16	17	18	0	
35)	50	34	0	0	0	0	0	Frozen, 52
36)	51	0	0	0	0	0	0	Fish, 53
37)	52	53	0	0	0	0	0	
38)	52	53	0	0	0	0	0	
39)	10	54	55	0	0	0	0	
40)	28	12	13	0	0	0	0	
41)	28	12	0	0	0	0	0	
42)	28	14	15	0	0	0	0	Characteristics, 12
43)	28	0	0	0	0	0	0	
44)	28	56	0	0	0	0	0	Birds, 28
45)	28	4	57	56	0	0	0	
46)	28	56	0	0	0	0	0	
47)	28	0	0	0	0	0	0	
48)	58	0	0	0	0	0	0	
49)	58	28	13	0	0	0	0	
50)	59	0	0	0	0	0	0	
51)	28	60	0	0	0	0	0	
52)	28	20	60	8	61	0	0	

53)	13	62	0	0	0	0	0	Bat, 62	Birds, 28
54)	62	60	0	0	0	0	0		
55)	62	61	0	0	0	0	0		
56)	4	12	13	0	0	0	0		
57)	62	0	0	0	0	0	0		
58)	58	63	0	0	0	0	0		
59)	28	13	12	0	0	0	0		
60)	27	64	44	49	18	0	0	Warm-blooded, 27	
61)	65	66	0	0	0	0	0		
62)	28	27	0	0	0	0	0		
63)	28	67	34	0	0	0	0		
64)	26	67	0	0	0	0	0		
65)	59	68	0	0	0	0	0	Feet, 59	
66)	59	68	28	3	0	0	0		
67)	3	69	68	70	71	0	0		
68)	28	71	72	73	74	0	0		
69)	59	6	75	0	0	0	0		
70)	76	59	77	0	0	0	0		
71)	78	79	3	0	0	0	0		
72)	3	0	0	0	0	0	0		
73)	80	59	0	0	0	0	0		
74)	59	81	80	6	0	0	0		
75)	58	23	24	0	0	0	0		
76)	12	82	0	0	0	0	0	Reptiles, 82	
77)	82	30	0	0	0	0	0		
78)	82	83	0	0	0	0	0		

79)	48	80	0	0	0	0	0		
80)	82	84	85	0	0	0	0		
81)	86	0	0	0	0	0	0		
82)	87	88	0	0	0	0	0		
83)	87	88	0	0	0	0	0		
84)	31	88	82	87	80	48	84	Lizard, 88	Reptiles, 82
85)	82	89	0	0	0	0	0		
86)	90	91	48	0	0	0	0		
87)	82	92	93	0	0	0	0		
88)	82	0	0	0	0	0	0	Reptiles, 82	
89)	82	30	0	0	0	0	0		
90)	82	12	0	0	0	0	0		
91)	12	0	0	0	0	0	0		
92)	30	12	0	0	0	0	0		
93)	23	82	0	0	0	0	0	Lungs, 44	
94)	82	49	0	0	0	0	0		
95)	82	49	0	0	0	0	0	Breathe, 49	
96)	82	94	44	0	0	0	0		
97)	64	82	95	96	88	44	97		
98)	31	82	28	13	0	0	0		
99)	39	31	0	0	0	0	0	Heart, 39	
100)	39	98	0	0	0	0	0	Blood, 43	
101)	98	40	82	0	0	0	0		
102)	99	43	98	0	0	0	0		
103)	85	43	0	0	0	0	0		
104)	40	39	43	48	0	0	0		

105)	100	43	44	0	0	0	0	
106)	43	48	45	0	0	0	0	
107)	31	45	0	0	0	0	0	
108)	98	39	45	0	0	0	0	
109)	82	14	101	0	0	0	0	
110)	83	84	0	0	0	0	0	
111)	84	82	0	0	0	0	0	
112)	84	102	80	0	0	0	0	
113)	103	88	87	80	82	84	0	Amphibians, 84
114)	84	80	0	0	0	0	0	
115)	84	69	94	44	0	0	0	
116)	84	69	104	94	0	0	0	
117)	69	44	105	0	0	0	0	

APPENDIX B

Transcript T-1 and Related Materials

Transcript T-1

1.	. . . was the relationship between plants and animals and their environment or the interaction between plants and animals and their environment.	1, 2, 3, 4
2.	And we discussed the different levels of interaction, all right, the levels of organization.	6, 5, 4
3.	And what was the first level of organization or interaction?	5, 6, 4
----	Atoms and molecules.	
4.	All right, atoms and molecules, and remember when we talked about chemistry, we had the interaction between enzymes and substrates.	7, 9, 12, 10, 11, 4
5.	That's an example of how the atoms and the molecules interact and will determine in part the chemistry and the organization of the plants and animals.	7, 9, 12, 1, 2, 4, 8
6.	But beyond that, once you have this chemistry, all these atoms and molecules form cells.	12, 7, 8, 13, 9
7.	All right, so we have an interaction between the cells.	4, 13
8.	Now, can you think back, when we studied the organization of the cell, how could you get an interaction?	13, 8, 4
9.	What structures did we study that could have taken part in interaction between the cells?	14, 4, 13
10.	There's some structure that looks like it could connect two different cells and form a pathway from one cell to another cell. M——?	14, 13
----	The endoplasmic reticulum.	
11.	All right, the endoplasmic reticulum, remember that?	15
12.	This is your cell membrane.	16
13.	And here's your nuclear membrane.	17
14.	Then we have these little wiggly double membranes.	18

15.	And we have pores in the nuclear membrane and pores in the cellular membrane.	19, 17, 16
16.	And these were called endoplasmic reticulum.	15
17.	And the ribosomes were located on them.	15, 20
18.	I know, we discussed how maybe these could be used in transport from one cell to another.	21, 13
19.	Maybe it's used in this interaction between the two cells.	15, 13, 4
20.	All right, what's another way in which two cells might interact or tell, one cell to tell another cell what's going on?	13, 4
21.	What type of cells are used in the communication between one part of the body and another part? S——?	13, 23, 22
----	Tissues.	
22.	All right, well, the cells make up the tissues but we have the nervous system.	24, 13, 26
23.	All right, these nerve cells connect, are connected to each other so that you have something happening on your finger.	26, 27, 28
24.	And it tells your brain that you better get your finger out of there.	27, 29, 28
25.	All right, so we have the cells forming the tissues, and then the tissues forming what?	13, 24
----	Uh . . .	
26.	A group of tissues form—?	24
----	Uh . . .	
27.	A group of tissues?	24
----	Organs.	
28.	All right, an organ, and the organs form an organ system.	30, 31
29.	And then we get to the individual.	32
30.	All right, but what about the individual by himself?	32
31.	Now you can have interaction between individuals. A——?	4, 32
----	. . . species . . . they know . . .	
32.	All right, if you had a group of individuals you form a species, right.	32, 33
33.	All right, and what was the definition of the species?	33
----	A living mate that gives fertile offspring.	

34.	All right, if two organisms—?	32
35.	All right, two organisms that mate and produce live fertile offspring are in the same species.	32, 34, 35, 37, 38, 33
36.	All right, and the lab that we just did was the interaction within a species—the effect on population growth that the death rate had or whether the death rate was the parents or the offspring or both.	4, 33, 40, 42, 38, 87
37.	All right, and the birth rate also affects the population growth.	43, 40
38.	So if you have a constant birth rate and you lower the death rate, what's going to happen to the population growth?	43, 42, 40
39.	All right, the population growth will increase.	40
40.	Anybody who doesn't see that?	40
41.	You have the same birth rate in two populations.	43, 39
42.	And one population has a lower death rate, all right?	39, 42
43.	This is why we're having population explosions.	42, 45
44.	Our birth rate hasn't changed that much.	43
45.	But we've cut the death rate.	42
46.	And above the species—we have groups of species interacting.	33, 4
47.	All right, they form a community.	46, 33
48.	What's an example of a community?	46
49.	What's an example of a community organization?	47
----	Birds?	
50.	The biosphere is the collection of all these communities.	48, 46
----	Jungle or the ocean.	
51.	All right, the ocean or lake, or jungle.	49, 50, 51
----	Garden.	
52.	All right, a garden, a garden's a community.	52, 46
53.	What interactions between what organisms take place in a garden?	4, 32, 52
----	Flowers and trees.	
54.	All right, flowers and trees, but, uh, do they interact?	53, 54, 4
55.	Do you think there's much interaction between flowers and trees? What type?	4, 53, 54

---- . . . .

56.	Oh, so the flowers with the flowers, but how about the flowers with the trees?	53, 54
----	Uh, you have small insects, worms.	
57.	All right, insects, worms, lots of microscopic organisms in the soil. And then, above the community, was the biosphere.	55, 56, 57, 46, 48, 58
58.	All right, but especially in regard to the activities which took place in the news this morning we're going to have to increase our biosphere eventually.	48
59.	We're going to have to include something that's going to take in the universe.	59
60.	If we start playing around the moon we're liable to find lots of things up there that we haven't found down here.	60
61.	From the filmstrip on the introduction to ecology they mentioned the factors that influence this interaction that are not living—all right?—the abiotic factors.	61, 4, 36, 62
62.	What were some of those?	62
63.	What are abiotic factors that have an effect on the interaction between two species or two individuals?	62, 4, 33, 32
----	. . . .	
64.	The amount of water?	63
----	Presence of . . .	
65.	Right, presence of water.	63
----	The atmosphere and the land.	
66.	The atmosphere, the land.	64, 65
----	The climate.	
67.	The climate. All right, so you have the idea of what these abiotic factors are.	66, 62
68.	The amount of rain is going to have a direct influence on the type of plants that are present. The amount of sunlight, the length of the day.	67, 1, 68, 69
69.	All right, and the type of plants that are present is going to have an influence on what animals are present.	1, 2
70.	But they are also biotic factors.	1, 2, 70

71.	And what are biotic factors?	70
72.	What's another way biotic factors influence interaction?	70, 4
----	Living?	
73.	All right, factors that have to do with living.	70, 36
74.	What factors between individuals have a direct effect on this interaction?	70, 32, 4
75.	The influence of one individual on another.	32
76.	And there are various ways in which this can take place.	32
77.	You can have an influence of the ancestors.	71
78.	All right, what are ways in which ancestors can influence you?	71
----	The structure of your body, functions of parts of your body.	
79.	All right, the inherited characteristics, all right, so you have inheritance taking place here.	73, 74
80.	Now, what about inheritance?	74
81.	Do you think it all has to be genetic?	74, 76
----	Environment?	
82.	All right, but I'm talking about inheritance here, uh, a passing of traits from one generation to another.	74, 88, 146
83.	We have genetic inheritance, in our genes.	76, 123
84.	Do you think that who your ancestors are has influenced you in any way besides just what you have inherited in your genes?	71, 74, 123
85.	Does anybody think that it has influence in any other way?	71
----	S—— said–	
----	"Environment," and you said she was wrong.	
86.	All right, maybe I didn't understand the way S—— used "environment."	3
87.	All right, you can have a cultural inheritance which is the environment ancestors set up.	77, 3, 71
88.	Man has evolved culturally a lot faster than he has genetically.	78, 79, 147
89.	I mean you have people coming together and transmitting ideas.	78

90.	All right, once they started to write, our ancestors passed things down to us.	71
91.	What they learned we didn't have to learn.	71, 81
92.	All we had to do was read it and go on from there.	81
93.	All right, so the ancestors influenced us.	71
94.	Then you have an interspecies influence.	80
95.	What does "inter" mean?	85
96.	What's the difference between "inter" and "intra"?	85, 86, 33
97.	Inter and intra—the species influence.	85, 86, 33
----	Interspecies is within one species. . . .	
98.	All right, it's just the opposite.	80
99.	The intra is the influence of two individuals in the same species upon one another, the influence of two people upon one another, the influence of two birds.	86, 32, 33, 82, 78
100.	Interspecies is the influence of an organism in one species upon an organism in a different species.	80, 32, 33
101.	All right, the influence on man of plants, on man of a bird, birds and worms, are interspecies influence.	78, 1, 82, 56, 80
----	Intraspecies—interspecies is the influence of an organism in one species on an organism in a different species.	
102.	And the intra is the influence of organisms in the same species upon one another.	86, 32, 33
103.	And then the last type of biotic influence would be the influence of organisms that are separated by large distances in the biosphere.	70, 32
104.	What's an example of the influence of organisms that are separated by large distances in the biosphere?	32, 48
----	. . . .	
105.	All right, just think of man.	78
----	Well, it could be the difference in the culture.	
106.	All right, the difference in the culture will have, uh, how's that going to affect you?	84, 78
----	. . . .	
107.	But why will that affect you?	84, 78
108.	What difference does it make if they have a culture?	78, 84

----	Well, it could have influence on us because we could learn from them.	
109.	All right, if we have contact some way, some type of communication, this might be an influence.	23
110.	And the way that we operate our culture right now, there are inflences interculturally.	84
111.	All right, but if something happens. Suppose China drops the bomb on Saigon—do you think that's going to affect us? All right.	23
112.	Now we'll go back and look at these different types of biotic factors in more detail.	70
113.	First we'll look at the ancestral influence.	71
114.	Later on this semester we'll talk about inheritance and genetics in more detail.	74, 147
115.	But I think that you all know, the basic idea behind inheritance, that you inherit different traits or different chemical compositions or capacity from each of your parents.	74, 88, 75, 87
116.	And we'll go into this in more detail later on.	74, 88, 75, 87
117.	This is basically what inheritance is.	74, 88, 75, 87
118.	It's the passing down of traits.	74, 88
119.	Well, what type of things would you inherit then?	74
120.	Or what types of things won't you inherit? P——?	74
121.	What types of things do you inherit?	74
----	Eye color.	
122.	All right, eye color. J——?	89
----	Hair color.	
123.	Hair color. P——?	90
----	Skin color.	
124.	All right, skin color. S——?	91
----	The X and Y chromosome . . . might have a tendency to	
125.	OK, but that would have an effect though that's the chemical effect.	12
----	Well, that's OK.	

126.	Right. All right, your body chemistry to a large extent is inherited.	93, 74
127.	But the environment—all right, what you inherit is only a limit and then your environment acts upon the limit to determine exactly where you're going to fall.	3, 74
128.	If you take for example IQ, all right, let's say you inherit a range—what you inherit won't say that you will have an IQ above a certain point.	94, 74
129.	But you probably won't have an IQ below a certain point.	94
130.	And then your environment, how you grow up, what influences you have as you're growing up, is going to determine more precisely where you fall.	3
131.	This is an interaction between the genetic inheritance and your environment—your cultural inheritance.	4, 76, 3, 77
132.	All right, behavior is inherited—behavior in birds.	95, 74
133.	And I have an article that has to do with the inheritance of behavior in lovebirds.	74, 95, 96
134.	All right, did you know that there was such a thing as a lovebird, a real one?	96
135.	All right, they're parrots, or related to the parrots, in the picture of different species of lovebirds.	96, 97, 33
136.	You can see that they look a lot like parrots.	96, 97
137.	Now they can trace the evolution of the lovebirds on the basis of their behavior.	98, 96, 95
138.	All right, down here [on the chart]—these are the primitive forms, the first ones in the evolution.	96, 99, 98
139.	And then it goes up, till these were the intermediate.	96, 115
140.	These are called the peach-faced lovebirds.	96, 117
141.	And then you have the most advanced over here, this group of four.	112, 96
142.	Now the behavior involved, for one thing the sexual behavior of these animals, has evolved. And their sexual pattern, all right, the patterns that they go through in their courtship, all right, in the early forms—the primitive forms down here [on the chart]—in their courtship behavior both the male and the female feed each other.	95, 101, 2, 98, 102, 99, 103, 105, 104

143.	All right, they exchange berries.	103, 105, 106, 104
144.	But then when in the peach-face, the peach-face lovebird, only the male feeds the female.	117, 105, 106, 104
145.	The female does not feed the male back.	105, 103, 104
146.	But she responds by fluffing up her feathers.	105, 122, 107
147.	Then, the more advanced, similar to the peach-face, but there's an evolution from this male and female giving of the berry till just the male is involved.	112, 117, 98, 103, 105, 106
148.	There's also an evolution of the nest-making.	98, 109
149.	First of all, the primitive forms, they both make nests in a hole.	99, 116
150.	All right, all of them make a nest in a hole.	99, 116
151.	But the primitive forms stay in pairs.	99
152.	And you just have the male and the female together.	103, 105
153.	The more advanced, the evolutionarily more advanced, live in colonies.	112, 110
154.	Their whole groups, their social groups are formed in the more advanced.	112, 111
155.	The primitive forms pick up little pieces of paper and bark and punch holes in them. So it looks sort of like a paper towel or a saltine cracker which has all little holes in it.	99, 113
156.	Then the bird fluffs up her feathers and puts these little pieces of bark and paper in between the feathers and then flies to where she's building her nest and takes the pieces of paper out and uses them to make her nest.	122, 82, 113, 107, 148, 116
157.	All right, so she puts all the pieces of paper in between her feathers.	105, 107
158.	Now the peach-face—we're just talking about the primitive forms, these four down here—the peach-face cuts longer strips, makes a neater nest, punches little holes in and instead of fluffing up all her feathers to put the bark or the paper in she just fluffs up the ones in the back and then sticks these in.	117, 99, 116, 122
159.	These are longer. And a lot of them fall out before she gets to the nest.	105, 116

160.	It's not as efficient as the other way. But they still use this method.	105
161.	Now, what do you think, if you follow this evolution, what do you think is the behavior of the most evolutionarily advanced in regards to this nest-gathering?	98, 95, 112, 118
162.	Now here we have the small bits of paper behind all the feathers carried to the nest.	107, 116
163.	Here you have longer strips put in the rear feathers.	107
164.	But it's very inefficient because she loses a lot of these pieces of paper and bark before she even gets to the nest.	105, 113, 116
165.	If you learn, these birds can pass this experience along. S——, what do you think the next step may be?	81, 82, 149
166.	All right. They go back to using small pieces. What else?	97
167.	How do most birds take their materials to the nest?	82
----	. . . .	
168.	All right, in their beaks. So the next step is that the most advanced carry the materials like most birds, in their beaks, to the nest.	119, 112, 82
169.	Now, if this is inherited, and we cross a bird, a peach-faced bird, with a higher bird that carries the material in the beak, what type of behavior would you expect?	82, 117, 119, 95
----	. . . .	
170.	All right, to a certain extent, right, the environment or what it would learn will influence what will happen.	3, 81, 82
171.	And it'll have the ability to do both.	82
172.	It has the innate capacity to do both.	82
173.	All right, well they actually did this and they were closely related enough so that they had produced live offspring which they could study.	82, 35, 36, 38
174.	The offspring weren't fertile.	37, 38
175.	These [parents] are of two different species.	33, 87
176.	What happened was that the offspring was confused.	38

177.	And when it came time to build a nest, it would run	38, 116
178.	And it wasn't really sure what it was supposed to do.	38
179.	Here it had one notion it wanted to carry it around in its beak, another notion to fluff up its wings and stick the bark and the paper between the wings.	38, 119, 113, 122, 121
180.	So it acted confused.	38
181.	It did a little bit of both.	38
182.	And it would fluff up its wings and carry it in its beak.	121, 122, 119
183.	And the ones that did try to stick the paper or bark in the wings and carry it, lost it all.	38, 113, 121
184.	They never were able to carry it to the nest.	38, 113, 116
185.	They had an innate capacity or felt compelled to stick these pieces in their wings and fly away and carry them to their nests.	38, 113, 121 116
186.	But they were never capable of actually reaching the nest.	38, 116
187.	So that over a period, it took two years for the birds to finally realize that they didn't have to stick these things in their feathers.	82, 113, 107
188.	They went through stages, trying to stick it in the feathers and fly, never reaching the nest.	82, 107, 116, 113
189.	And then they'd go through all the motions of sticking it in the feathers but actually carrying it in their beak.	82, 113, 119
190.	Then gradually the amount of effort they put into sticking it in their feathers and fluffing up the feathers decreased.	107, 122, 82
191.	And they would just carry it in their beak.	82, 119
192.	And after two years then they gave up trying to fluff up their feathers at all.	82, 122, 107
193.	And they would just carry it in their beak.	82, 119
194.	But here you have this conflict between what was inherited genetically and what they actually learned.	76, 81
195.	And it's also a good illustration of how learning works from the genetic material.	81, 123
196.	The genetic material is just the basis upon which the learning experience can work.	123, 81

197.	It determines your capacity within limits.	123
198.	But then it's what you learn and your experiences in the environment that really have the greatest effect.	81, 3
199.	All right, another example of how ancestors have an influence besides the lovebirds can be with mice, or rats actually.	71, 96, 124, 125
200.	They've done experiments with rat populations in which you have one population where the rats are more efficient and they're healthier and they live here.	125, 39
201.	Then there are other populations all around. They're less efficient.	39
202.	All right, they're not as big.	39
203.	They're not as healthy.	39, 126
204.	If you have a fight, these guys are always going to win.	127, 39
205.	Their colony grows faster.	39, 110
206.	Then you take these individuals or even offspring of these individuals and put them in another population.	32, 38
207.	And there they become the leaders.	32, 128
208.	There's an inherited leadership ability or an inherited strength here.	128, 74
209.	And you can't really draw any profound conclusions from it because the environment has a tremendous effect.	128, 74, 3
210.	All right, I don't know whether you remember the first day or the second day I mentioned the effect of environment on IQ—just the simple fact of having a mother or when you're young having care and protection, the tremendous effect that it has on IQ, so that there's a question now whether anything about IQ is inherited.	3, 94, 44, 74
211.	Maybe it's the total environment.	74, 3, 94
212.	And yet not too many people are willing to admit that.	74, 3, 94
213.	But the wide range of inheritance of IQ—the environment plays the biggest effect.	74, 94, 3
214.	All right, next I want to look at the intraspecies.	83
215.	What is the intraspecies?	83

216.	How could you say it in other words? T——?	83
217.	What's intraspecies?	83
----	When two individuals are . . .	
218.	All right, but what about the individuals?	32
219.	Are they in the same species?	32, 33
----	. . . .	
	B——?	
----	In same species.	
220.	In the same species. All right, think of it—international.	33
221.	Inter means between.	85
222.	This is between two species—international, intercommunication, uh— What's another one?	80, 33
----	Interact.	
223.	All right, interact. You have two people interacting.	4
224.	It's between.	4
225.	This intra is within. All right—same species.	86, 33
226.	And this is interaction between individuals in the same species.	4, 32, 33
227.	You have a group of birds and you know the birds are capable of, physiologically, producing a large number of eggs.	82, 136, 35, 129, 38
228.	All right, but there's only a certain amount of food for this whole population in this given area, so that if each of them has five offspring maybe they'll just be scrawny.	150, 39, 38
229.	And more of them will die because there won't be enough food.	38, 131, 150
230.	But if each of them has three, it can have three healthy ones instead of five scrawny ones.	38, 126
231.	And this is more efficient.	38, 126
232.	If you have five scrawny ones, each of them is more susceptible to being killed by disease or by having a cat catch them.	38, 138, 130
233.	They can't fly very fast and are caught by a cat.	38, 148
234.	But if they have three healthy ones, these birds that can reproduce over again or that can survive through disease or some cold weather, this is more efficient.	38, 126, 82, 151, 132, 130

235.	So what you have is an interaction of a number of birds within a given area.	4, 82
236.	And it limits the number of eggs that the females actually produce.	4, 82, 105, 35, 129
237.	All right, this happens with other animals.	2, 105, 35, 129
238.	If you create an overpopulated community of mice you'll have a reduction in the birth rate.	133, 46, 43, 124
239.	You have a lot of other effects of crowding.	152
240.	All right, the effects of crowding are being studied in great detail lately where animals—and then people postulate, well, what effect does crowding have in the major cities with human beings?	152, 2, 78, 155
241.	Can you take the effects that you get in experiments with other animals and say, well then, maybe this happens with human beings?	2, 78
242.	I mean does that make—do you think that's a good idea?	2, 78
243.	Do you like the idea of being called an animal . . . everybody else?	2, 78
----	. . . .	
244.	All right, well, we do have a brain which is a brain[?] in the power of communication, the power of speech.	78, 153, 29, 23
245.	All right, it is the biggest difference between man and other animals.	153, 2, 78
246.	But, what we have to remember is that if you agree with the theory of evolution we have come down from other animals that don't speak.	100, 2, 78, 153
247.	And we still are animals. So we still are influenced to a certain degree. You're right.	78, 2
248.	But you can postulate and say it might have some effect on us.	78
249.	When you take mice—all right, mice are pretty far removed from us.	124, 78
250.	But if you take an elephant—all right, an elephant is a mammal.	134, 135
251.	And it's, you know, as far as mammals go, an advanced mammal.	135

252.	All right, in the Philadelphia zoo they've done experiments with an overcrowded state of these elephants.	145, 133, 134
253.	The elephants don't have enough room to move around, and [they] get crowded.	134, 152
254.	All right, and what happens is a breakdown in the whole physiology of the animal.	134, 136
255.	They have heart attacks.	134, 137
256.	No, no reason can be found except for the effect of the crowding on the elephants.	134, 152
257.	With mice you have like a fight—for no reason, just to fight and try and kill each other.	124, 127
258.	Or else they become completely the other way like a paranoid.	124, 154
259.	And they just sit in the corner and won't talk to anyone. All right, so that they won't even know anybody's there.	124
260.	They act as if—like they're mentally disturbed.	124
261.	All right, they just sit there and won't interact.	124, 4
262.	And it all points to an effect of crowding—so now there are all sorts of postulates, postulates going on as to what effect the city has upon man.	152, 78, 155
263.	Now there's a lot of crowding effects in the city.	155, 152
264.	Does it affect the birth rate?	152, 43
265.	Are people producing weaker young?	78, 38
266.	Does it affect them and how they interact with other people?	38, 4, 78
267.	Does part of the crime in the city have to do with the crowding?	155, 152
268.	These are things that people that are studying animal behavior are talking about.	140
269.	This is a whole new field of biology.	140, 139
270.	It's called ethology.	140
271.	It's the study of animal behavior.	140
272.	And it's a really interesting field for anyone who's interested.	140
273.	Uh, a big name and one of the early workers in this was Konrad Lorenz.	140

274.	The trouble with a lot of scientists when they write is that they only write for other scientists.	144
275.	And he has other books like *On Aggression.* And then there's that other book that I mentioned to you about, uh, territorial imperative.	141
276.	And this has to do with the animal behavior.	141, 140
277.	Tomorrow I have a short filmstrip on the community, all right?—A fresh-water and a salt-water community.	46, 142, 143

Kinetogram Summary Table for Transcript T-1

Mean Fundamental Coefficient	Mean Weighted Coefficient
0.41	0.90
Total Number of Discourse Units	Total Frequency of Elements
277	622
Number of Primary Spans	Primary Span Mean Length
5	48
Number of Secondary Spans	Secondary Span Mean Length
32	9

	Origin	*Conclusion*	$\bar{B}_1$	$\bar{B}_2$	*Verbal Elements*	*Transition*	*TAC*
Primary Span							
1	1	35	0.39	0.94	Interaction, 4 Cells, 13		
2	36	104	0.33	0.87	Biotic factor, 70	C-2	0.27
3	105	131	0.39	0.91	Inherit, 74	C-3	0.63
4	132	193	0.38	0.87	Bird, 82	C-2	0.23
5	227	267	0.42	0.89	Man, 78	NC	–
Secondary Span							
1	1	5	0.53	0.92	Atoms, 7 Molecule, 9		
2	6	10	0.61	0.93	Cells, 13		
3	11	17	0.10	0.92	Endoplasmic reticulum, 15		
4	18	24	0.42	0.91	Cells, 13		
5	25	28	0.42	0.93	Tissues, 24		
6	29	35	0.47	0.88	Organism, 32		
7	36	40	0.53	0.91	Population growth, 40		
8	41	46	0.17	0.87	Death rate, 42		
9	47	60	0.21	0.91	Community, 46		
10	61	67	0.26	0.88	Abiotic, 62		
11	68	76	0.52	0.92	Biotic factors, 70		
12	77	93	0.35	0.88	Ancestors, 71		
13	94	104	0.31	0.87	Species, 33		
14	105	113	0.30	0.89	Man, 78		
15	114	121	0.70	0.95	Inherit, 74		
16	122	131	0.21	0.89	Intelligence quotient, 94		
17	132	141	0.51	0.92	Lovebird, 96		
18	142	164	0.30	0.88	Primitive form, 99		
19	165	173	0.37	0.89	Birds, 82		
20	174	186	0.43	0.88	Offspring, 38		
21	187	193	0.42	0.89	Birds, 82		

	Origin	Conclusion	$\bar{B}_1$	$\bar{B}_2$	Verbal Elements
Secondary Span					
22	194	198	0.43	0.90	Learn, 81
23	199	207	0.50	0.92	Population, 39
24	208	213	0.79	0.96	Environment, 3
25	214	226	0.44	0.88	Species, 33
26	227	234	0.42	0.90	Offspring, 38
27	235	239	0.31	0.87	Birds, 82
28	240	249	0.68	0.96	Animals, 2
29	250	256	0.37	0.92	Elephant, 134
30	257	261	0.55	0.94	Mice, 124
31	262	267	0.35	0.85	Crowding, 152
32	268	277	0.50	0.95	Ethology, 140
Gain Series:					
Artificial linear	93	97	0.30	0.89	
Real linear	199	202	0.50	0.92	
	208	212	0.75	0.96	
	227	231	0.46	0.89	
	238	241	0.33	0.89	
	257	260	0.52	0.95	
Decay Series:					
Real linear	203	207	0.49	0.93	
Symmetries:					
Real, four-point	49	52	0.00	0.89	
Real, three-point	191	193	0.40	0.90	
	271	273	1.00	1.00	

DISTRIBUTION OF FUNDAMENTAL COEFFICIENTS

Interval	*Percentage of Coefficients Occurring in Each Interval*
0.000–0.095	32.85
0.096–0.195	0.00
0.196–0.295	5.05
0.296–0.395	5.77
0.396–0.495	9.02
0.496–0.595	14.44
0.596–0.695	14.07
0.696–0.795	0.72
0.796–0.895	5.77
0.896–1.000	11.91

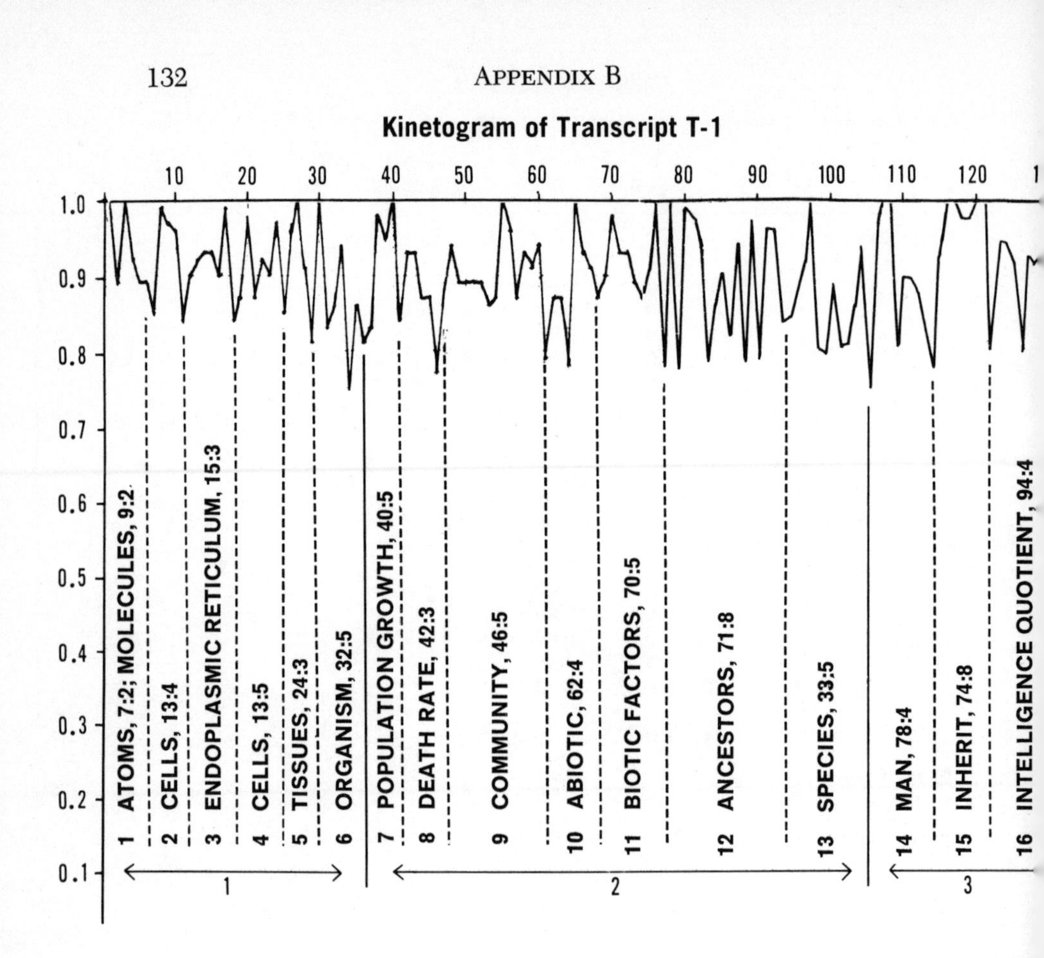
Kinetogram of Transcript T-1
1 ATOMS, 7:2; MOLECULES, 9:2
2 CELLS, 13:4
3 ENDOPLASMIC RETICULUM, 15:3
4 CELLS, 13:5
5 TISSUES, 24:3
6 ORGANISM, 32:5
7 POPULATION GROWTH, 40:5
8 DEATH RATE, 42:3
9 COMMUNITY, 46:5
10 ABIOTIC, 62:4
11 BIOTIC FACTORS, 70:5
12 ANCESTORS, 71:8
13 SPECIES, 33:5
14 MAN, 78:4
15 INHERIT, 74:8
16 INTELLIGENCE QUOTIENT, 94:4
1
2
3

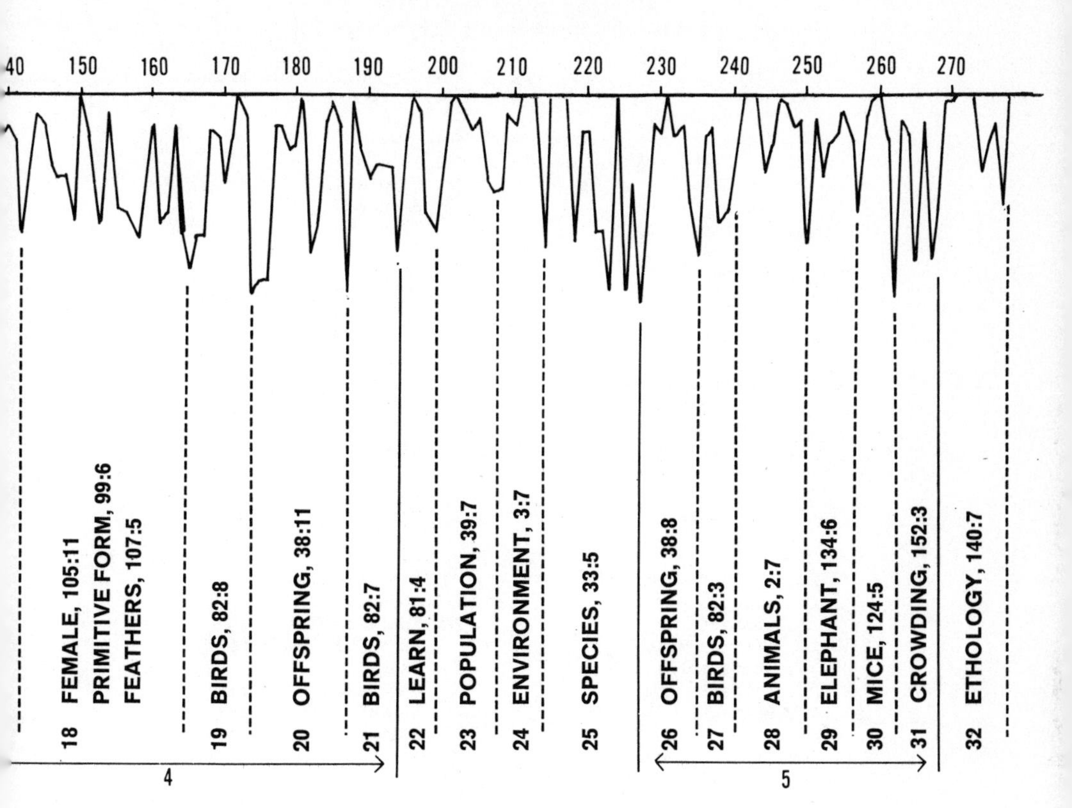
40
150
160
170
180
190
200
210
220
230
240
250
260
270
18 FEMALE, 105:11
PRIMITIVE FORM, 99:6
FEATHERS, 107:5
19 BIRDS, 82:8
20 OFFSPRING, 38:11
21 BIRDS, 82:7
22 LEARN, 81:4
23 POPULATION, 39:7
24 ENVIRONMENT, 3:7
25 SPECIES, 33:5
26 OFFSPRING, 38:8
27 BIRDS, 82:3
28 ANIMALS, 2:7
29 ELEPHANT, 134:6
30 MICE, 124:5
31 CROWDING, 152:3
32 ETHOLOGY, 140:7
4
5

Coded Elements of Transcript T-1

1. Plants
2. Animals
3. Environment
4. Interaction = relationship
5. Level of organization
6. Level
7. Atoms
8. Organization
9. Molecules
10. Enzyme
11. Substrate
12. Chemistry
13. Cells
14. Structures
15. Endoplasmic reticulum
16. Cell membrane = cellular membrane
17. Nuclear membrane
18. Double membrane
19. Pores
20. Ribosomes
21. Transport
22. Body
23. Communication
24. Tissue
25. Connect
26. Nervous system
27. Nerve cells
28. Finger
29. Brain
30. Organ
31. Organ system
32. Individual = organism
33. Species
34. Mate
35. Produce
36. Live = living
37. Fertile
38. Offspring
39. Population
40. Population growth
41. Growth, grow
42. Death rate
43. Birth rate
44. Mother
45. Population explosion
46. Community
47. Community organization
48. Biosphere
49. Ocean
50. Lake
51. Jungle
52. Garden
53. Flowers
54. Trees
55. Insects
56. Worms
57. Microscopic organisms
58. Soil
59. Universe
60. Moon
61. Ecology
62. Abiotic
63. Water
64. Atmosphere
65. Land
66. Climate
67. Rain
68. Sunlight
69. Day
70. Biotic factors
71. Ancestors
72. Functions
73. Inherited characteristics
74. Inherit
75. Chemical composition
76. Genetic inheritance
77. Cultural inheritance
78. Man = people
79. Evolve
80. Interspecies
81. Learn
82. Birds
83. Intraspecies
84. Culture
85. Inter-
86. Intra-
87. Parent
88. Trait = characteristic
89. Eye color
90. Hair color
91. Skin color
92. Chromosomes
93. Body chemistry

94. IQ
95. Behavior
96. Lovebird
97. Parrots
98. Evolution
99. Primitive form
100. Theory of evolution
101. Sexual behavior = sexual pattern
102. Courtship = courtship behavior
103. Male
104. Feed
105. Female
106. Berries
107. Feathers
108. Response
109. Nest-making
110. Colonies
111. Social group
112. Advanced (in evolution)
113. Bark (tree)
114. Weather
115. Intermediate (in evolution)
116. Nest
117. Peach-face = peach-face lovebird
118. Nest-gathering
119. Beak
120. Cross (breed)
121. Wings
122. Fluff
123. Genetic material
124. Mice
125. Rats
126. Health
127. Fight
128. Leader
129. Eggs
130. Disease
131. Die
132. Survive
133. Overpopulated
134. Elephant
135. Mammal
136. Physiology
137. Heart attack
138. Kill
139. Biology
140. Ethology
141. Territorial imperative
142. Fresh-water community
143. Salt-water community
144. Scientist
145. Zoo
146. Generation
147. Genetically
148. Fly (on wing)
149. Experience
150. Food
151. Reproduce
152. Crowding
153. Speech
154. Paranoid
155. City

Fundamental Coefficients for Transcript T-1

Discourse Unit	B_1	Discourse Unit	B_1	Discourse Unit	B_1
2	0.29	24	0.67	46	0.0
3	1.0	25	0.0	47	0.50
4	0.22	26	0.67	48	0.67
5	0.62	27	1.0	49	0.0
6	0.50	28	0.0	50	0.0
7	0.29	29	0.0	51	0.0
8	0.80	30	1.0	52	0.0
9	0.67	31	0.67	53	0.40
10	0.80	32	0.50	54	0.33
11	0.0	33	0.67	55	1.0
12	0.0	34	0.0	56	0.80
13	0.0	35	0.29	57	0.0
14	0.0	36	0.33	58	0.33
15	0.0	37	0.25	59	0.0
16	0.0	38	0.80	60	0.0
17	0.67	39	0.50	61	0.0
18	0.0	40	1.0	62	0.40
19	0.40	41	0.0	63	0.40
20	0.80	42	0.50	64	0.0
21	0.40	43	0.50	65	1.0
22	0.33	44	0.0	66	0.0
23	0.33	45	0.0	67	0.0

Discourse Unit	B_1	Discourse Unit	B_1	Discourse Unit	B_1
68	0.0	91	0.67	114	0.0
69	0.33	92	0.67	115	0.33
70	0.80	93	0.0	116	1.0
71	0.50	94	0.0	117	1.0
72	0.67	95	0.0	118	0.67
73	0.50	96	0.50	119	0.67
74	0.40	97	1.0	120	1.0
75	0.50	98	0.0	121	1.0
76	1.0	99	0.0	122	0.0
77	0.0	100	0.50	123	0.0
78	1.0	101	0.25	124	0.0
79	0.0	102	0.25	125	0.0
80	0.67	103	0.40	126	0.0
81	0.67	104	0.50	127	0.50
82	0.40	105	0.0	128	0.50
83	0.0	106	0.67	129	0.67
84	0.40	107	1.0	130	0.0
85	0.50	108	1.0	131	0.40
86	0.0	109	0.0	132	0.0
87	0.50	110	0.0	133	0.80
88	0.0	111	0.0	134	0.50
89	0.50	112	0.0	135	0.50
90	0.0	113	0.0	136	0.80

Discourse Unit	B_1	Discourse Unit	B_1	Discourse Unit	B_1
137	0.40	160	0.67	183	0.33
138	0.67	161	0.0	184	0.67
139	0.40	162	0.0	185	0.86
140	0.50	163	0.67	186	0.67
141	0.50	164	0.0	187	0.0
142	0.0	165	0.0	188	0.86
143	0.46	166	0.0	189	0.57
144	0.75	167	0.0	190	0.33
145	0.57	168	0.50	191	0.40
146	0.33	169	0.57	192	0.40
147	0.22	170	0.29	193	0.40
148	0.25	171	0.50	194	0.0
149	0.0	172	1.0	195	0.50
150	1.0	173	0.50	196	1.0
151	0.67	174	0.0	197	0.67
152	0.0	175	0.0	198	0.0
153	0.0	176	0.0	199	0.0
154	0.50	177	0.67	200	0.33
155	0.0	178	0.67	201	0.67
156	0.25	179	0.33	202	1.0
157	0.25	180	0.33	203	0.67
158	0.0	181	1.0	204	0.50
159	0.33	182	0.0	205	0.50

Discourse Unit	B_1	Discourse Unit	B_1	Discourse Unit	B_1
206	0.40	230	0.40	254	0.50
207	0.40	231	1.0	255	0.50
208	0.50	232	0.40	256	0.50
209	0.80	233	0.40	257	0.0
210	0.57	234	0.25	258	0.40
211	0.86	235	0.25	259	0.67
212	1.0	236	0.57	260	1.0
213	1.0	237	0.67	261	0.67
214	0.0	238	0.0	262	0.0
215	1.0	239	0.0	263	0.80
216	1.0	240	0.40	264	0.50
217	1.0	241	0.67	265	0.0
218	0.0	242	1.0	266	0.80
219	0.67	243	1.0	267	0.0
220	0.67	244	0.33	268	0.0
221	0.0	245	0.57	269	0.67
222	0.0	246	0.86	270	0.67
223	0.0	247	0.67	271	1.0
224	1.0	248	0.67	272	1.0
225	0.0	249	0.67	273	1.0
226	0.40	250	0.0	274	0.0
227	0.0	251	0.67	275	0.0
228	0.25	252	0.0	276	0.67
229	0.67	253	0.40	277	0.0

Code Summary Sheet for Transcript T-1

										Group	Overall
1)	1	2	3	4	0	0	0	0	0	Atoms, 7 Molecule, 9	Interaction, 4 Cells, 13
2)	6	5	4	0	0	0	0	0	0		
3)	6	5	4	0	0	0	0	0	0		
4)	7	9	12	10	11	4	0	0	0		
5)	7	9	12	1	2	4	8	0	0		
6)	7	8	12	13	9	0	0	0	0	Cells, 13	
7)	4	13	0	0	0	0	0	0	0		
8)	4	8	13	0	0	0	0	0	0		
9)	4	13	14	0	0	0	0	0	0		
10)	13	14	0	0	0	0	0	0	0		
11)	15	0	0	0	0	0	0	0	0	Endoplasmic reticulum, 15	
12)	16	0	0	0	0	0	0	0	0		
13)	17	0	0	0	0	0	0	0	0		
14)	18	0	0	0	0	0	0	0	0		
15)	16	17	19	0	0	0	0	0	0		
16)	15	0	0	0	0	0	0	0	0		
17)	15	20	0	0	0	0	0	0	0		

18)	13	21	0	0	0	0	0	0	0	Cells, 13
19)	4	13	15	0	0	0	0	0	0	
20)	4	13	0	0	0	0	0	0	0	
21)	13	22	23	0	0	0	0	0	0	
22)	13	24	26	0	0	0	0	0	0	
23)	26	27	28	0	0	0	0	0	0	
24)	27	28	29	0	0	0	0	0	0	
25)	13	24	0	0	0	0	0	0	0	Tissues, 24
26)	24	0	0	0	0	0	0	0	0	
27)	24	0	0	0	0	0	0	0	0	
28)	30	31	0	0	0	0	0	0	0	
29)	32	0	0	0	0	0	0	0	0	Organism, 32
30)	32	0	0	0	0	0	0	0	0	
31)	4	32	0	0	0	0	0	0	0	
32)	32	33	0	0	0	0	0	0	0	
33)	33	0	0	0	0	0	0	0	0	
34)	32	0	0	0	0	0	0	0	0	
35)	32	34	35	33	37	38	0	0	0	
36)	4	33	40	42	38	87	0	0	0	

37)	43	40	0	0	0	0	0	0	0	Population growth, 40
38)	43	42	40	0	0	0	0	0	0	
39)	40	0	0	0	0	0	0	0	0	
40)	40	0	0	0	0	0	0	0	0	
41)	43	39	0	0	0	0	0	0	0	Death rate, 42
42)	39	42	0	0	0	0	0	0	0	
43)	42	45	0	0	0	0	0	0	0	
44)	43	0	0	0	0	0	0	0	0	
45)	42	0	0	0	0	0	0	0	0	
46)	4	33	0	0	0	0	0	0	0	
47)	33	46	0	0	0	0	0	0	0	Community, 46
48)	46	0	0	0	0	0	0	0	0	
49)	47	0	0	0	0	0	0	0	0	
50)	46	48	0	0	0	0	0	0	0	
51)	49	50	51	0	0	0	0	0	0	
52)	46	52	0	0	0	0	0	0	0	
53)	4	32	52	0	0	0	0	0	0	
54)	4	53	54	0	0	0	0	0	0	
55)	4	53	54	0	0	0	0	0	0	

56)	53	54	0	0	0	0	0	0	0	
57)	55	56	57	46	48	0	0	0	0	
58)	48	0	0	0	0	0	0	0	0	
59)	59	0	0	0	0	0	0	0	0	
60)	60	0	0	0	0	0	0	0	0	
61)	4	36	61	62	0	0	0	0	0	
62)	62	0	0	0	0	0	0	0	0	
63)	62	4	32	33	0	0	0	0	0	
64)	63	0	0	0	0	0	0	0	0	Abiotic, 62
65)	63	0	0	0	0	0	0	0	0	
66)	64	65	0	0	0	0	0	0	0	
67)	62	66	0	0	0	0	0	0	0	
68)	1	67	68	69	0	0	0	0	0	
69)	1	2	0	0	0	0	0	0	0	
70)	1	2	70	0	0	0	0	0	0	
71)	70	0	0	0	0	0	0	0	0	Biotic
72)	4	70	0	0	0	0	0	0	0	factors, 70
73)	70	36	0	0	0	0	0	0	0	
74)	4	32	70	0	0	0	0	0	0	

75)	32	0	0	0	0	0	0	0	0	
76)	32	0	0	0	0	0	0	0	0	
77)	71	0	0	0	0	0	0	0	0	Ancestors, 71
78)	71	0	0	0	0	0	0	0	0	
79)	73	74	0	0	0	0	0	0	0	
80)	74	0	0	0	0	0	0	0	0	
81)	74	76	0	0	0	0	0	0	0	
82)	74	88	146	0	0	0	0	0	0	
83)	76	123	0	0	0	0	0	0	0	
84)	71	74	123	0	0	0	0	0	0	
85)	71	0	0	0	0	0	0	0	0	
86)	3	0	0	0	0	0	0	0	0	
87)	3	71	77	0	0	0	0	0	0	
88)	78	79	147	0	0	0	0	0	0	
89)	78	0	0	0	0	0	0	0	0	
90)	71	0	0	0	0	0	0	0	0	
91)	71	81	0	0	0	0	0	0	0	
92)	81	0	0	0	0	0	0	0	0	
93)	71	0	0	0	0	0	0	0	0	

Biotic factor, 70

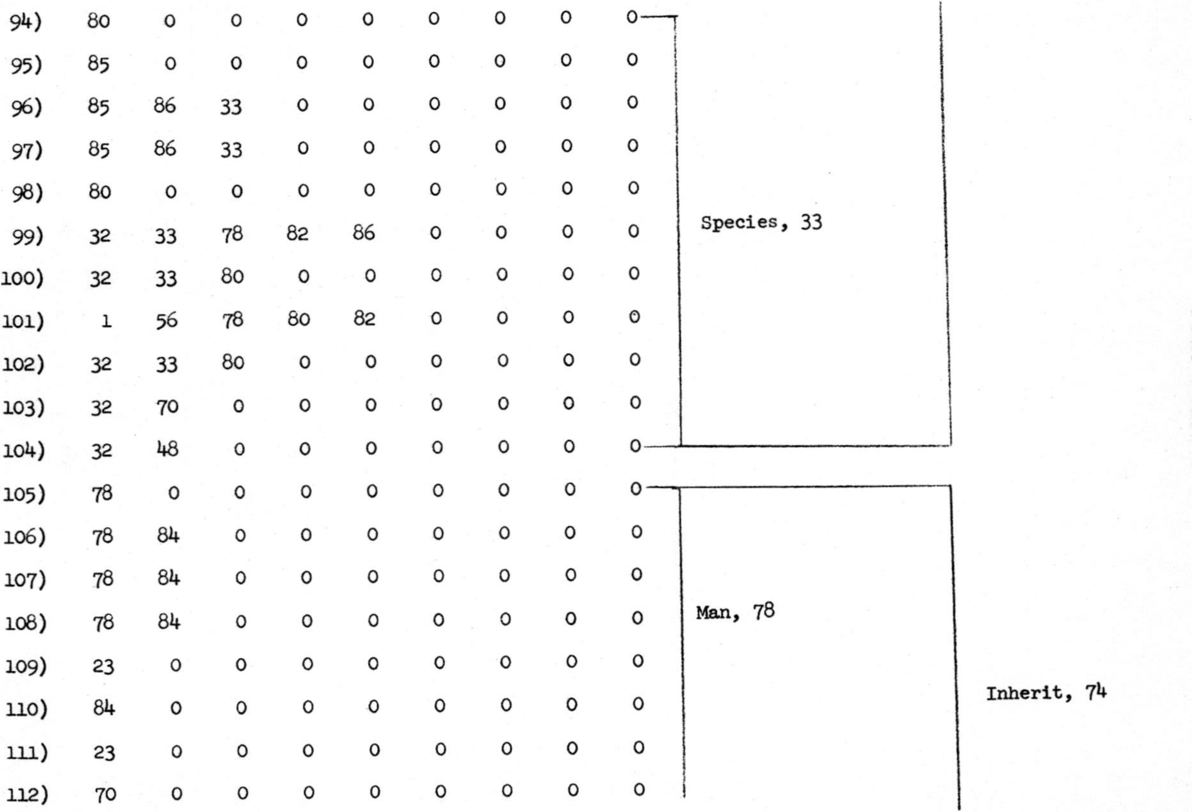

94)	80	0	0	0	0	0	0	0	0	0
95)	85	0	0	0	0	0	0	0	0	0
96)	85	86	33	0	0	0	0	0	0	0
97)	85	86	33	0	0	0	0	0	0	0
98)	80	0	0	0	0	0	0	0	0	0
99)	32	33	78	82	86	0	0	0	0	0
100)	32	33	80	0	0	0	0	0	0	0
101)	1	56	78	80	82	0	0	0	0	0
102)	32	33	80	0	0	0	0	0	0	0
103)	32	70	0	0	0	0	0	0	0	0
104)	32	48	0	0	0	0	0	0	0	0
105)	78	0	0	0	0	0	0	0	0	0
106)	78	84	0	0	0	0	0	0	0	0
107)	78	84	0	0	0	0	0	0	0	0
108)	78	84	0	0	0	0	0	0	0	0
109)	23	0	0	0	0	0	0	0	0	0
110)	84	0	0	0	0	0	0	0	0	0
111)	23	0	0	0	0	0	0	0	0	0
112)	70	0	0	0	0	0	0	0	0	0

113)	71	0	0	0	0	0	0	0	0	
114)	74	147	0	0	0	0	0	0	0	
115)	74	75	87	88	0	0	0	0	0	
116)	74	75	87	88	0	0	0	0	0	
117)	74	75	87	88	0	0	0	0	0	
118)	74	88	0	0	0	0	0	0	0	Inherit, 74
119)	74	0	0	0	0	0	0	0	0	
120)	74	0	0	0	0	0	0	0	0	
121)	74	0	0	0	0	0	0	0	0	
122)	89	0	0	0	0	0	0	0	0	
123)	90	0	0	0	0	0	0	0	0	
124)	91	0	0	0	0	0	0	0	0	
125)	12	0	0	0	0	0	0	0	0	
126)	74	93	0	0	0	0	0	0	0	Intelligence quotient, 94
127)	3	74	0	0	0	0	0	0	0	
128)	74	94	0	0	0	0	0	0	0	
129)	94	0	0	0	0	0	0	0	0	
130)	3	0	0	0	0	0	0	0	0	
131)	3	4	76	77	0	0	0	0	0	

132)	74	95	0	0	0	0	0	0	0	
133)	74	95	96	0	0	0	0	0	0	
134)	96	0	0	0	0	0	0	0	0	
135)	33	96	97	0	0	0	0	0	0	
136)	96	97	0	0	0	0	0	0	0	
137)	95	96	98	0	0	0	0	0	0	Love bird, 96
138)	96	98	99	0	0	0	0	0	0	
139)	96	115	0	0	0	0	0	0	0	
140)	96	117	0	0	0	0	0	0	0	
141)	96	112	0	0	0	0	0	0	0	
142)	95	101	2	98	102	99	103	105	104	
143)	103	104	105	106	0	0	0	0	0	
144)	104	105	106	117	0	0	0	0	0	
145)	103	104	105	0	0	0	0	0	0	Primitive form, 99
146)	105	107	122	0	0	0	0	0	0	
147)	98	103	105	106	112	117	0	0	0	
148)	98	109	0	0	0	0	0	0	0	
149)	99	116	0	0	0	0	0	0	0	
150)	99	116	0	0	0	0	0	0	0	

151)	99	0	0	0	0	0	0	0	0		Birds, 82
152)	103	105	0	0	0	0	0	0	0		
153)	110	112	0	0	0	0	0	0	0		
154)	111	112	0	0	0	0	0	0	0		
155)	99	113	0	0	0	0	0	0	0		
156)	82	113	116	107	122	148	0	0	0		
157)	105	107	0	0	0	0	0	0	0		
158)	99	116	117	122	0	0	0	0	0		
159)	105	116	0	0	0	0	0	0	0		
160)	105	0	0	0	0	0	0	0	0		
161	95	98	112	118	0	0	0	0	0		
162)	107	116	0	0	0	0	0	0	0		
163)	107	0	0	0	0	0	0	0	0		
164)	105	113	116	0	0	0	0	0	0		
165)	81	82	149	0	0	0	0	0	0	Birds, 82	
166)	97	0	0	0	0	0	0	0	0		
167)	82	0	0	0	0	0	0	0	0		
168)	112	119	82	0	0	0	0	0	0		
169)	82	95	117	119	0	0	0	0	0		

170)	3	81	82	0	0	0	0	0	0	
171)	82	0	0	0	0	0	0	0	0	
172)	82	0	0	0	0	0	0	0	0	
173)	82	35	36	0	0	0	0	0	0	
174)	37	38	0	0	0	0	0	0	0	
175)	33	87	0	0	0	0	0	0	0	
176)	38	0	0	0	0	0	0	0	0	
177)	38	116	0	0	0	0	0	0	0	
178)	38	0	0	0	0	0	0	0	0	
179)	38	113	119	121	122	0	0	0	0	Offspring, 38
180)	38	0	0	0	0	0	0	0	0	
181)	38	0	0	0	0	0	0	0	0	
182)	119	121	122	0	0	0	0	0	0	
183)	38	113	121	0	0	0	0	0	0	
184)	38	113	116	0	0	0	0	0	0	
185)	38	113	116	121	0	0	0	0	0	
186)	38	116	0	0	0	0	0	0	0	
187)	82	113	107	0	0	0	0	0	0	
188)	82	107	113	116	0	0	0	0	0	

189)	82	113	119	0	0	0	0	0	0	Birds, 82
190)	82	107	122	0	0	0	0	0	0	
191)	82	119	0	0	0	0	0	0	0	
192)	82	122	107	0	0	0	0	0	0	
193)	82	119	0	0	0	0	0	0	0	
194)	76	81	0	0	0	0	0	0	0	Learn, 81
195)	81	123	0	0	0	0	0	0	0	
196)	81	123	0	0	0	0	0	0	0	
197)	123	0	0	0	0	0	0	0	0	
198)	81	3	0	0	0	0	0	0	0	
199)	71	96	124	125	0	0	0	0	0	Population, 39
200)	39	125	0	0	0	0	0	0	0	
201)	39	0	0	0	0	0	0	0	0	
202)	39	0	0	0	0	0	0	0	0	
203)	39	126	0	0	0	0	0	0	0	
204)	39	127	0	0	0	0	0	0	0	
205)	39	110	0	0	0	0	0	0	0	
206)	32	38	39	0	0	0	0	0	0	
207)	32	128	0	0	0	0	0	0	0	

208)	74	128	0	0	0	0	0	0	0	Environment, 3
209)	3	74	128	0	0	0	0	0	0	
210)	3	44	74	94	0	0	0	0	0	
211)	3	74	94	0	0	0	0	0	0	
212)	3	74	94	0	0	0	0	0	0	
213)	3	74	94	0	0	0	0	0	0	
214)	83	0	0	0	0	0	0	0	0	Species, 33
215)	83	0	0	0	0	0	0	0	0	
216)	83	0	0	0	0	0	0	0	0	
217)	83	0	0	0	0	0	0	0	0	
218)	32	0	0	0	0	0	0	0	0	
219)	32	33	0	0	0	0	0	0	0	
220)	33	0	0	0	0	0	0	0	0	
221)	85	0	0	0	0	0	0	0	0	
222)	33	80	0	0	0	0	0	0	0	
223)	4	0	0	0	0	0	0	0	0	
224)	4	0	0	0	0	0	0	0	0	
225)	33	86	0	0	0	0	0	0	0	
226)	4	32	33	0	0	0	0	0	0	

										Group
227)	35	82	38	129	136	0	0	0	0	
228)	38	39	150	0	0	0	0	0	0	
229)	38	131	150	0	0	0	0	0	0	
230)	38	126	0	0	0	0	0	0	0	
231)	38	126	0	0	0	0	0	0	0	Offspring, 38
232)	38	130	138	0	0	0	0	0	0	
233)	38	148	0	0	0	0	0	0	0	
234)	38	82	126	130	132	151	0	0	0	
235)	4	82	0	0	0	0	0	0	0	
236)	4	35	82	105	129	0	0	0	0	
237)	35	105	129	2	0	0	0	0	0	Birds, 82
238)	43	46	124	133	0	0	0	0	0	
239)	152	0	0	0	0	0	0	0	0	
240)	2	78	152	155	0	0	0	0	0	
241)	2	78	0	0	0	0	0	0	0	
242)	2	78	0	0	0	0	0	0	0	
243)	2	78	0	0	0	0	0	0	0	
244)	78	23	29	153	0	0	0	0	0	Animals, 2
245)	2	78	153	0	0	0	0	0	0	

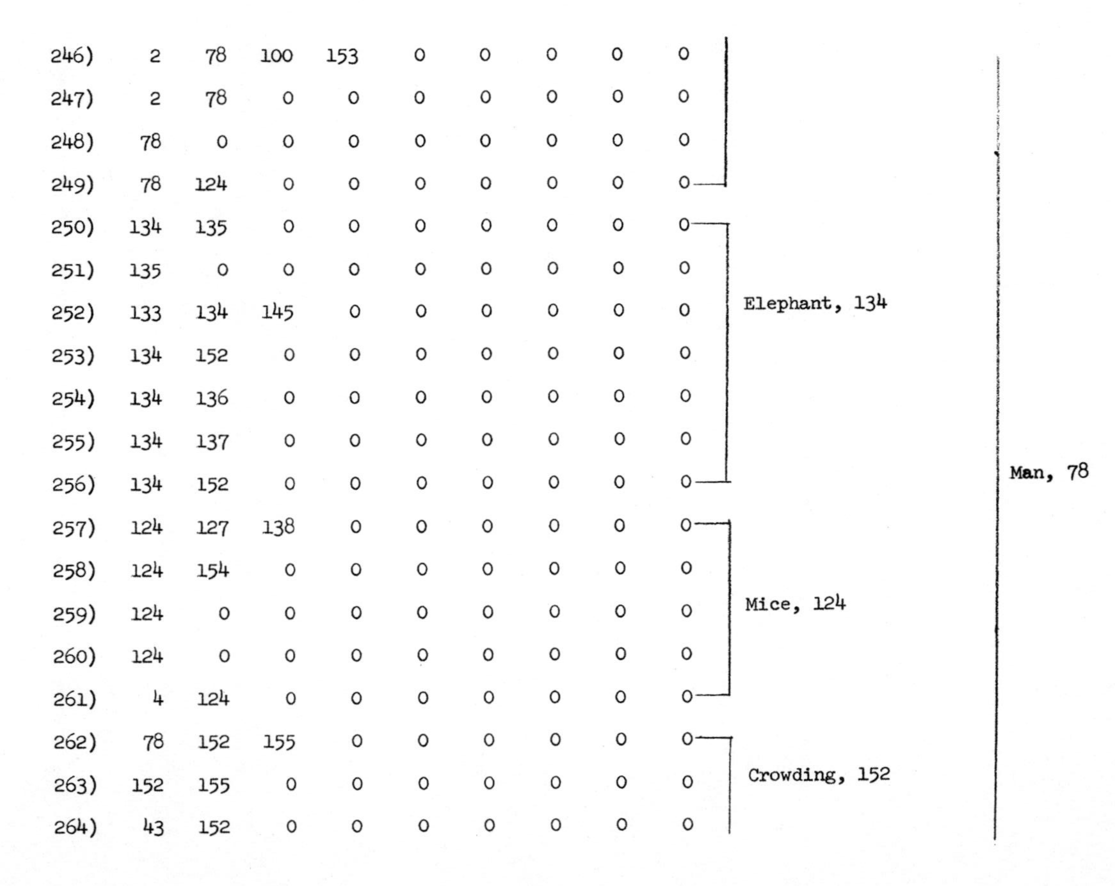

										Group	Group
246)	2	78	100	153	0	0	0	0	0		Man, 78
247)	2	78	0	0	0	0	0	0	0		Man, 78
248)	78	0	0	0	0	0	0	0	0		Man, 78
249)	78	124	0	0	0	0	0	0	0		Man, 78
250)	134	135	0	0	0	0	0	0	0	Elephant, 134	Man, 78
251)	135	0	0	0	0	0	0	0	0	Elephant, 134	Man, 78
252)	133	134	145	0	0	0	0	0	0	Elephant, 134	Man, 78
253)	134	152	0	0	0	0	0	0	0	Elephant, 134	Man, 78
254)	134	136	0	0	0	0	0	0	0	Elephant, 134	Man, 78
255)	134	137	0	0	0	0	0	0	0	Elephant, 134	Man, 78
256)	134	152	0	0	0	0	0	0	0	Elephant, 134	Man, 78
257)	124	127	138	0	0	0	0	0	0	Mice, 124	Man, 78
258)	124	154	0	0	0	0	0	0	0	Mice, 124	Man, 78
259)	124	0	0	0	0	0	0	0	0	Mice, 124	Man, 78
260)	124	0	0	0	0	0	0	0	0	Mice, 124	Man, 78
261)	4	124	0	0	0	0	0	0	0	Mice, 124	Man, 78
262)	78	152	155	0	0	0	0	0	0	Crowding, 152	Man, 78
263)	152	155	0	0	0	0	0	0	0	Crowding, 152	Man, 78
264)	43	152	0	0	0	0	0	0	0	Crowding, 152	Man, 78

265)	38	78	0	0	0	0	0	0	0
266)	4	38	78	0	0	0	0	0	0
267)	152	155	0	0	0	0	0	0	0
268)	140	0	0	0	0	0	0	0	0
269)	139	140	0	0	0	0	0	0	0
270)	140	0	0	0	0	0	0	0	0
271)	140	0	0	0	0	0	0	0	0
272)	140	0	0	0	0	0	0	0	0
273)	140	0	0	0	0	0	0	0	0
274)	144	0	0	0	0	0	0	0	0
275)	141	0	0	0	0	0	0	0	0
276)	140	141	0	0	0	0	0	0	0
277)	46	142	143	0	0	0	0	0	0

Ethology, 140

APPENDIX C

Kinetogram T-2 and Related Materials

Kinetogram Summary Table for Transcript T-2

Mean Fundamental Coefficient	Mean Weighted Coefficient
0.44	0.84
Total Number of Discourse Units	Total Frequency of Elements
175	405
Number of Primary Spans	Primary Span Mean Length
2	27
Number of Secondary Spans	Secondary Span Mean Length
16	11

	Origin	Conclusion	$\bar{B}_1$	$\bar{B}_2$	Verbal Elements	Transition	TAC
Primary Span							
1	123	147	0.40	0.84	Nucleus, 32		
2	148	175	0.43	0.80	Endospore, 77	C-2	0.27
Secondary Span							
1	1	9	0.48	0.81	Leeuwenhoek, 3		
2	10	14	0.48	0.87	Bacteria, 1		
3	15	20	0.52	0.82	Cohn, 82		
4	21	27	0.62	0.85	Unicellular organism, 7		
5	28	35	0.43	0.81	Virus, 18		
6	36	40	0.48	0.83	Microscope, 20		
7	41	48	0.54	0.85	Bacillus, 11 Spirilla, 23 Cocci, 22		
8	49	65	0.32	0.80	Structure, 25 Cytoplasm, 26		
9	66	82	0.60	0.91	Bacteria, 1 Capsule, 38		
10	83	91	0.53	0.84	Cell wall, 35		
11	92	107	0.46	0.85	Cell membrane, 33 Mitochondrion, 44		
12	108	122	0.33	0.87	Cytoplasm, 26		
13	123	129	0.45	0.88	Chromosome, 62		
14	130	147	0.39	0.83	Nucleus, 32		
15	148	161	0.47	0.84	Endospore, 77		
16	162	175	0.38	0.76	Spore, 70		
Gain Series:							
Artificial pulsed	149	159	0.43	0.84			

DISTRIBUTION OF FUNDAMENTAL COEFFICIENTS

Interval	*Percentage of Coefficients Occurring in Each Interval*
0.000–0.095	22.28
0.096–0.195	0.00
0.196–0.295	4.00
0.296–0.395	8.57
0.396–0.495	12.00
0.496–0.595	24.00
0.596–0.695	12.00
0.696–0.795	1.14
0.796–0.895	5.71
0.896–1.000	9.71

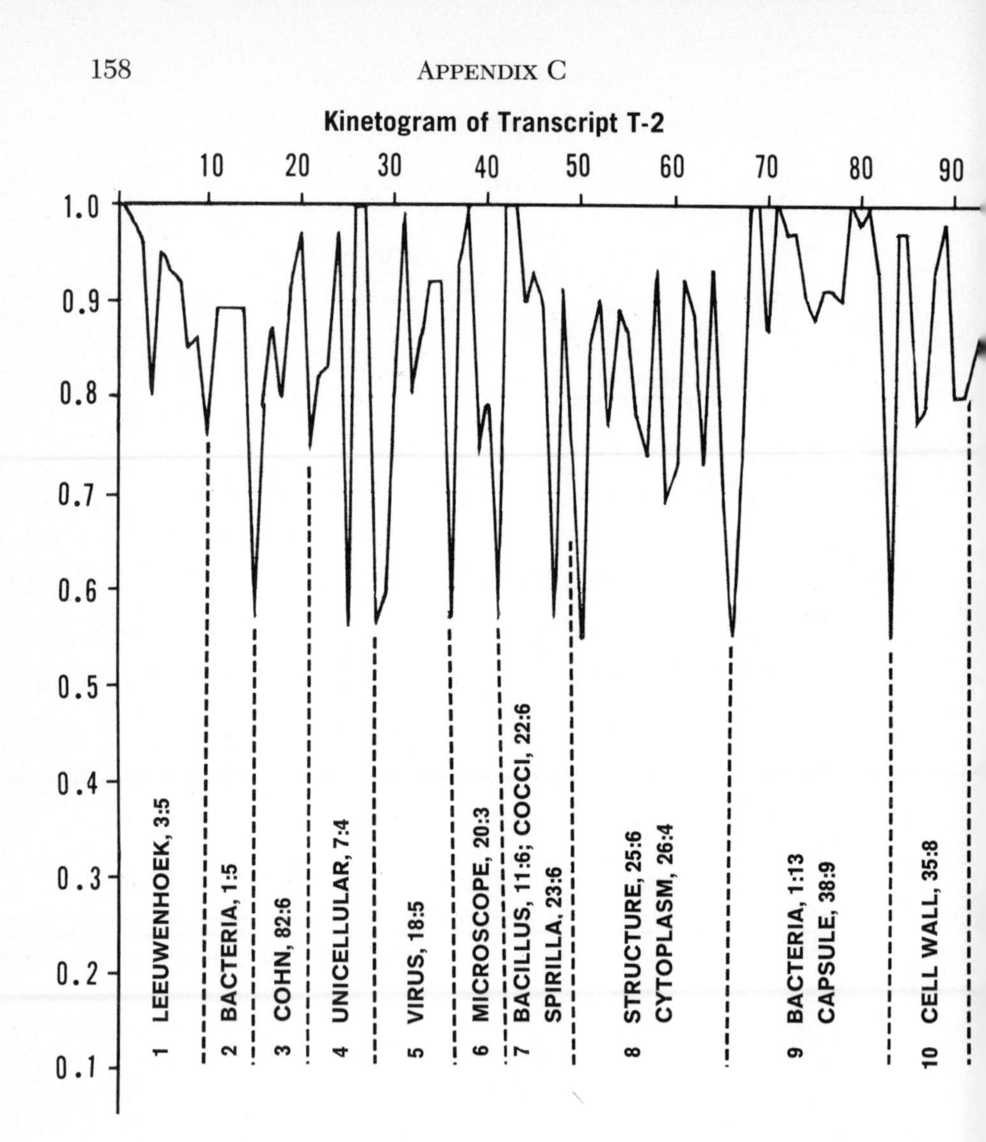
Kinetogram of Transcript T-2
10
20
30
40
50
60
70
80
90
1.0
0.9
0.8
0.7
0.6
0.5
0.4
0.3
0.2
0.1
1 LEEUWENHOEK, 3:5
2 BACTERIA, 1:5
3 COHN, 82:6
4 UNICELLULAR, 7:4
5 VIRUS, 18:5
6 MICROSCOPE, 20:3
7 BACILLUS, 11:6; COCCI, 22:6
SPIRILLA, 23:6
8 STRUCTURE, 25:6
CYTOPLASM, 26:4
9 BACTERIA, 1:13
CAPSULE, 38:9
10 CELL WALL, 35:8

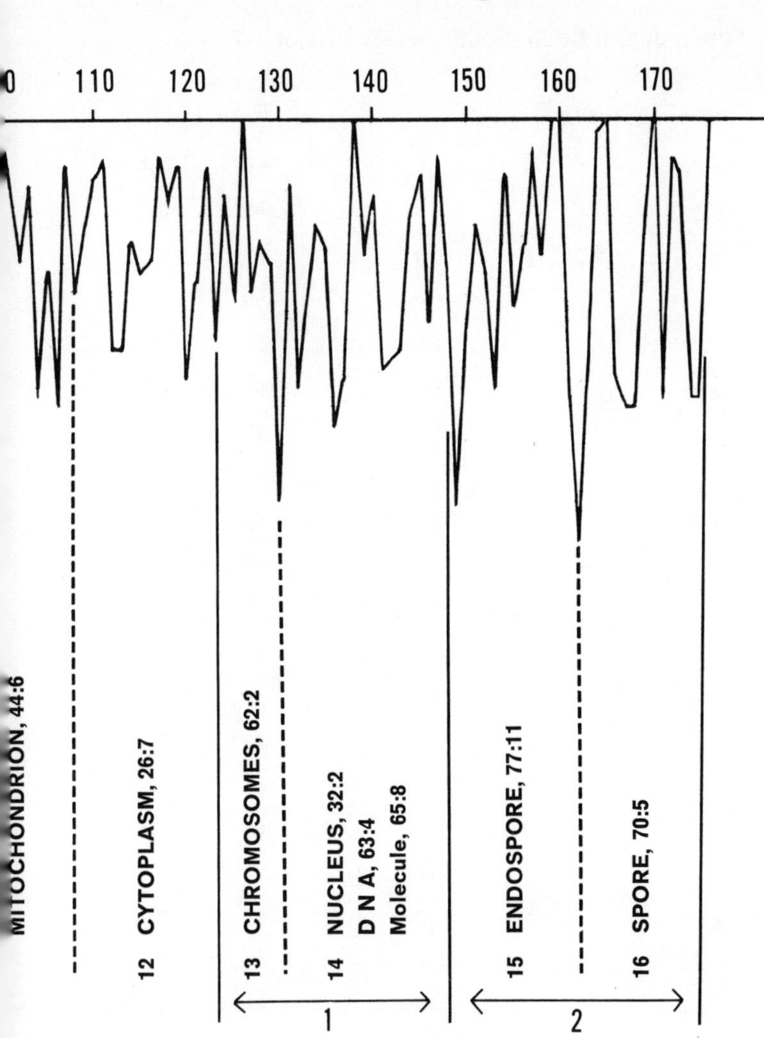
110
120
130
140
150
160
170
MITOCHONDRION, 44:6
12 CYTOPLASM, 26:7
13 CHROMOSOMES, 62:2
14 NUCLEUS, 32:2
D N A, 63:4
Molecule, 65:8
15 ENDOSPORE, 77:11
16 SPORE, 70:5
1
2

Fundamental Coefficients for Transcript T-2

Discourse Unit	B_1	Discourse Unit	B_1	Discourse Unit	B_1
2	0.67	24	0.75	46	0.40
3	0.67	25	0.0	47	0.0
4	0.50	26	1.0	48	0.50
5	0.40	27	1.0	49	0.0
6	0.67	28	0.0	50	0.0
7	0.57	29	0.0	51	0.33
8	0.33	30	0.50	52	0.67
9	0.50	31	0.80	53	0.40
10	0.40	32	0.50	54	0.50
11	0.50	33	0.67	55	0.40
12	0.50	34	0.50	56	0.0
13	0.50	35	0.50	57	0.0
14	0.50	36	0.0	58	0.50
15	0.0	37	0.50	59	0.0
16	0.50	38	1.0	60	0.0
17	0.67	39	0.40	61	0.80
18	0.50	40	0.50	62	0.40
19	0.80	41	0.0	63	0.40
20	0.67	42	1.0	64	0.67
21	0.33	43	1.0	65	0.33
22	0.29	44	0.75	66	0.0
23	0.33	45	0.67	67	0.0

Discourse Unit	B_1	Discourse Unit	B_1	Discourse Unit	B_1
68	1.0	91	0.50	114	0.0
69	1.0	92	0.0	115	0.0
70	0.67	93	0.67	116	0.0
71	1.0	94	1.0	117	0.50
72	0.67	95	0.0	118	0.50
73	0.67	96	0.80	119	0.50
74	0.50	97	0.33	120	0.0
75	0.40	98	0.40	121	0.40
76	0.40	99	0.40	122	0.80
77	0.40	100	0.80	123	0.40
78	0.40	101	0.50	124	0.67
79	1.0	102	0.40	125	0.0
80	0.67	103	0.57	126	1.0
81	1.0	104	0.29	127	0.0
82	0.50	105	0.29	128	0.67
83	0.0	106	0.29	129	0.40
84	0.80	107	0.57	130	0.0
85	0.80	108	0.25	131	0.50
86	0.50	109	0.33	132	0.33
87	0.50	110	0.67	133	0.57
88	0.50	111	0.40	134	0.33
89	0.67	112	0.0	135	0.67
90	0.50	113	0.0	136	0.29

Discourse Unit	B_1	Discourse Unit	B_1
137	0.0	160	1.0
138	1.0	161	0.0
139	0.50	162	0.0
140	0.67	163	0.40
141	0.0	164	0.80
142	0.0	165	1.0
143	0.0	166	0.0
144	0.33	167	0.33
145	0.57	168	0.33
146	0.50	169	0.50
147	0.67	170	1.0
148	0.29	171	0.0
149	0.0	172	0.50
150	0.0	173	0.50
151	0.50	174	0.0
152	0.33	175	0.0
153	0.33		
154	0.50		
155	0.50		
156	0.33		
157	0.86		
158	0.40		
159	1.0		

APPENDIX D

Kinetogram T-3 and Related Materials

Kinetogram Summary Table for Transcript T-3

Mean Fundamental Coefficient	Mean Weighted Coefficient
0.38	0.85
Total Number of Discourse Units	Total Frequency of Elements
212	579
Number of Primary Spans	Primary Span Mean Length
3	44
Number of Secondary Spans	Secondary Span Mean Length
18	11

	Origin	*Conclusion*	$\bar{B}_1$	$\bar{B}_2$	*Verbal Elements*	*Transition*	*TAC*
Primary Span							
1	1	54	0.35	0.84	Heat, 8		
2	55	91	0.38	0.84	Refrigeration, 42	C-3	0.23
3	140	180	0.41	0.86	Glycolysis, 105	C-3	0.50
Secondary Span							
1	1	7	0.22	0.81	Heat, 8		
2	8	21	0.46	0.88	Endospore, 11 Acidic, 14		
3	22	26	0.39	0.84	Pressure, 20		
4	27	31	0.27	0.75	Organism, 5		
5	32	54	0.40	0.87	Pasteurization, 29 Milk, 28		
6	55	69	0.41	0.85	Microorganism, 6		
7	70	91	0.34	0.83	Freeze, 50 Food, 3		
8	92	109	0.56	0.90	Vitamins, 59		
9	110	119	0.40	0.90	Bacteria, 2		
10	120	126	0.52	0.87	Fermentation, 79		
11	127	131	0.17	0.83	Glucose, 83		
12	132	139	0.33	0.89	Electron transport, 58		
13	140	152	0.31	0.84	Fermentation, 79		
14	153	172	0.45	0.88	Glycolysis, 105		
15	173	180	0.47	0.86	Organism, 5		
16	181	190	0.51	0.89	Bacteria, 2 Humans, 112		
17	191	200	0.14	0.80	Alcohol, 100		
18	201	212	0.24	0.82	Fermentation, 79		
Gain Series:							
Artificial linear	13	16	0.47	0.88			
	92	95	0.25	0.79			
	150	156	0.46	0.89			
Real linear	56	59	0.49	0.89			

	Ori-gin	*Con-clu-sion*	$\bar{B}_1$	$\bar{B}_2$
Decay Series:				
Artificial linear	157	159	0.36	0.87
Real pulsed	125	129	0.33	0.86

DISTRIBUTION OF FUNDAMENTAL COEFFICIENTS

Interval	*Percentage of Coefficients Occurring in Each Interval*
0.000–0.095	27.35
0.096–0.195	0.00
0.196–0.295	9.90
0.296–0.395	12.26
0.396–0.495	14.62
0.496–0.595	10.37
0.596–0.695	9.90
0.696–0.795	1.88
0.796–0.895	6.13
0.896–1.000	7.07

Kinetogram of Transcript T-3

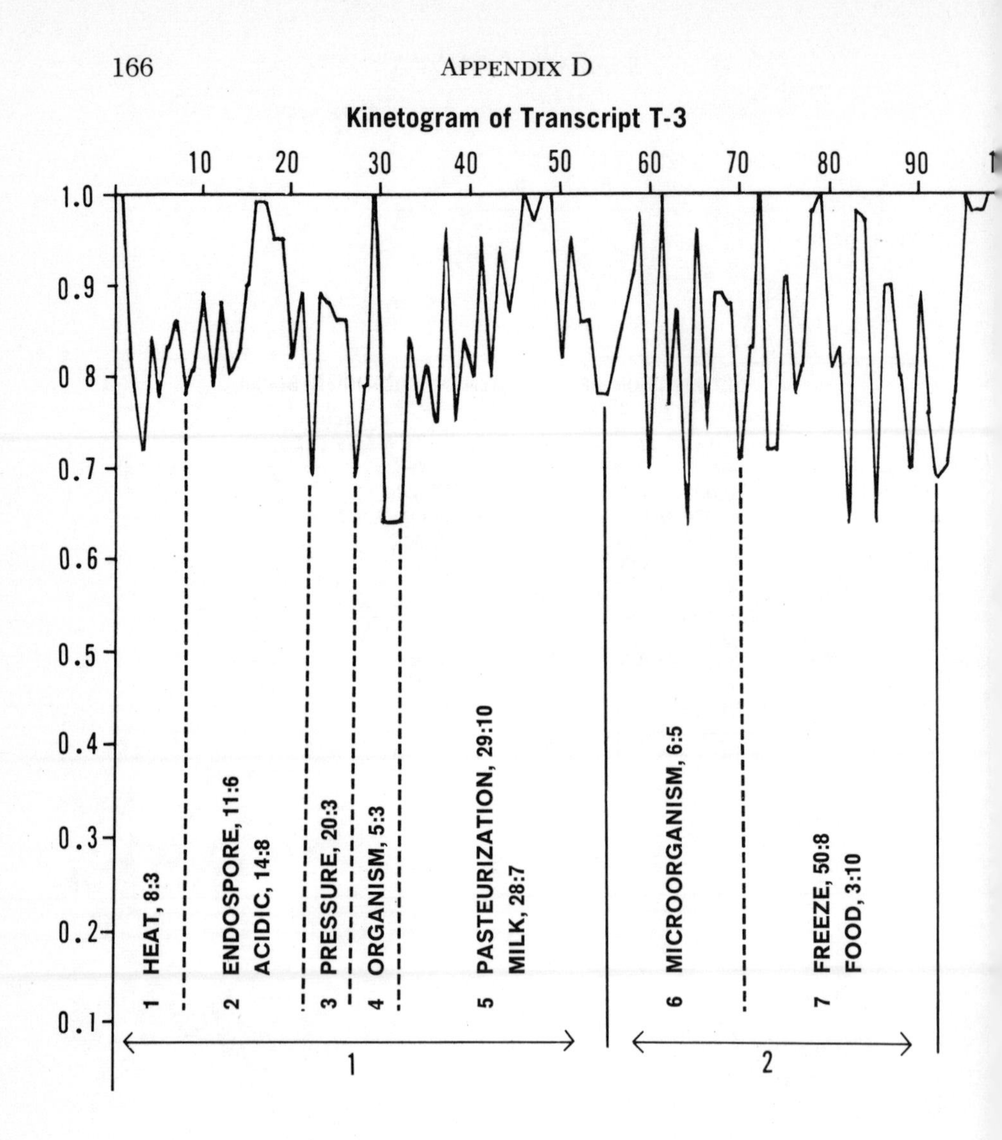

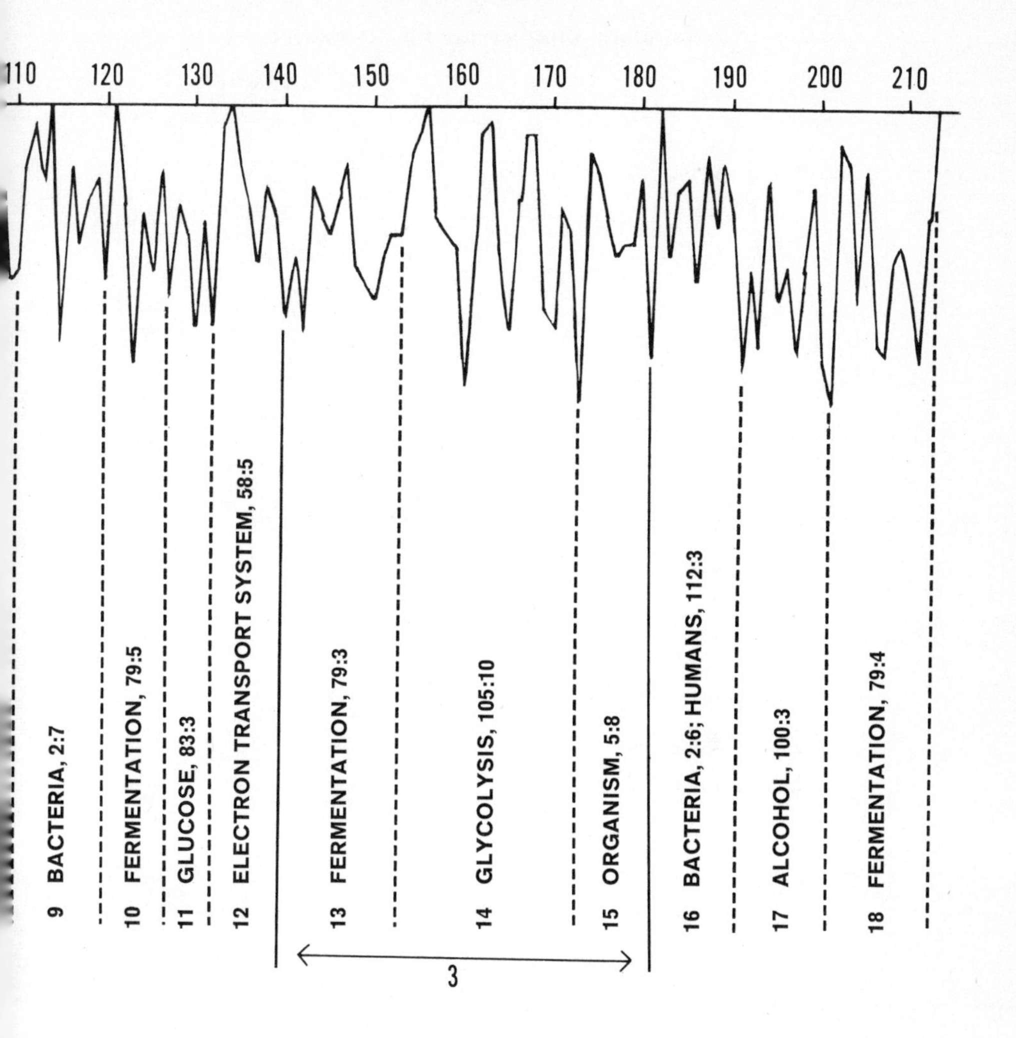
110
120
130
140
150
160
170
180
190
200
210
9 BACTERIA, 2:7
10 FERMENTATION, 79:5
11 GLUCOSE, 83:3
12 ELECTRON TRANSPORT SYSTEM, 58:5
13 FERMENTATION, 79:3
14 GLYCOLYSIS, 105:10
15 ORGANISM, 5:8
16 BACTERIA, 2:6; HUMANS, 112:3
17 ALCOHOL, 100:3
18 FERMENTATION, 79:4
3

Fundamental Coefficients for Transcript T-3

Discourse Unit	B_1	Discourse Unit	B_1	Discourse Unit	B_1
2	0.50	25	0.50	48	1.0
3	0.0	26	0.50	49	1.0
4	0.0	27	0.0	50	0.0
5	0.0	28	0.33	51	0.67
6	0.33	29	1.0	52	0.33
7	0.50	30	0.0	53	0.33
8	0.0	31	0.0	54	0.0
9	0.40	32	0.0	55	0.0
10	0.29	33	0.40	56	0.0
11	0.25	34	0.0	57	0.50
12	0.40	35	0.33	58	0.67
13	0.29	36	0.0	59	0.80
14	0.40	37	0.50	60	0.0
15	0.40	38	0.0	61	1.0
16	0.80	39	0.20	62	0.25
17	0.80	40	0.22	63	0.55
18	0.80	41	0.50	64	0.0
19	0.80	42	0.57	65	0.67
20	0.33	43	0.44	66	0.29
21	0.44	44	0.33	67	0.25
22	0.0	45	0.67	68	0.57
23	0.40	46	1.0	69	0.57
24	0.57	47	0.67	70	0.0

Discourse Unit	B_1	Discourse Unit	B_1	Discourse Unit	B_1
71	0.40	94	0.0	117	0.40
72	1.0	95	1.0	118	0.40
73	0.0	96	0.67	119	0.44
74	0.0	97	0.67	120	0.40
75	0.50	98	1.0	121	1.0
76	0.22	99	1.0	122	0.50
77	0.29	100	0.50	123	0.0
78	0.80	101	0.80	124	0.67
79	1.0	102	0.80	125	0.40
80	0.29	103	0.67	126	0.67
81	0.33	104	0.40	127	0.0
82	0.0	105	0.67	128	0.33
83	0.67	106	0.67	129	0.25
84	0.50	107	0.29	130	0.0
85	0.0	108	0.75	131	0.29
86	0.29	109	0.29	132	0.0
87	0.29	110	0.33	133	0.40
88	0.33	111	0.33	134	1.0
89	0.0	112	0.75	135	0.33
90	0.33	113	0.33	136	0.33
91	0.25	114	1.0	137	0.0
92	0.0	115	0.0	138	0.50
93	0.0	116	0.0	139	0.40

Discourse Unit	B_1	Discourse Unit	B_1	Discourse Unit	B_1
140	0.0	164	0.40	188	0.44
141	0.33	165	0.0	189	0.67
142	0.0	166	0.50	190	0.50
143	0.40	167	0.67	191	0.0
144	0.0	168	0.67	192	0.40
145	0.0	169	0.0	193	0.0
146	0.57	170	0.0	194	0.0
147	0.75	171	0.40	195	0.0
148	0.33	172	0.40	196	0.25
149	0.33	173	0.0	197	0.0
150	0.0	174	0.75	198	0.33
151	0.0	175	0.67	199	0.40
152	0.40	176	0.50	200	0.0
153	0.33	177	0.40	201	0.0
154	0.67	178	0.40	202	0.80
155	0.80	179	0.40	203	0.67
156	1.0	180	0.67	204	0.33
157	0.40	181	0.0	205	0.50
158	0.33	182	1.0	206	0.0
159	0.33	183	0.33	207	0.0
160	0.0	184	0.40	208	0.33
161	0.40	185	0.67	209	0.0
162	0.80	186	0.29	210	0.22
163	0.80	187	0.80	211	0.0
				212	0.0

APPENDIX E

Kinetogram T-4 and Related Materials

Kinetogram Summary Table for Transcript T-4

Mean Fundamental Coefficient	Mean Weighted Coefficient
0.38	0.90
Total Number of Discourse Units	Total Frequency of Elements
310	647
Number of Primary Spans	Primary Span Mean Length
6	48
Number of Secondary Spans	Secondary Span Mean Length
35	9

	Origin	*Conclusion*	$\bar{B}_1$	$\bar{B}_2$	*Verbal Elements*	*Transition*	*TAC*
Primary Span							
1	8	52	0.31	0.89	Coelenterate, 4		
2	53	69	0.25	0.89	Flatworm, 51	NC	–
3	70	105	0.38	0.90	Roundworm, 64	C-3	0.33
4	106	177	0.48	0.92	Mollusc, 82	NC	–
5	178	199	0.42	0.90	Annelid, 120	NC	–
6	200	293	0.40	0.89	Arthropod, 7	NC	–
Secondary Span							
1	1	7	0.16	0.84	Animal characteristics, 5		
2	8	12	0.63	0.97	Coelenterates, 4		
3	13	16	0.13	0.88	Animal symmetry, 10		
4	17	22	0.43	0.91	Animal, 14		
5	23	28	0.11	0.86	Enchinoderm, 16		
6	29	35	0.44	0.90	Sac-body, 25		
7	36	43	0.10	0.87	Coral, 31		
8	44	52	0.44	0.90	Sea anemone, 42		
9	53	61	0.07	0.87	Flatworm, 51		
10	62	69	0.43	0.90	Single-opening, 59		
11	70	74	0.20	0.85	Aschelminthes, 65		
12	75	80	0.11	0.81	Roundworm, 64		
13	81	85	0.47	0.94	Body opening, 26		
14	86	90	0.47	0.93	Eye dropper, 69		
15	91	99	0.44	0.91	Inside space, 72		
16	100	105	0.56	0.93	Vinegar eel, 79		
17	106	128	0.41	0.92	Mollusc shell, 83		
18	129	145	0.56	0.93	Abalone, 95		
19	146	158	0.57	0.94	Snail, 88		
20	159	168	0.48	0.92	Octopus, 111		
21	169	177	0.28	0.93	Cuttle bone, 115		
22	178	188	0.55	0.93	Segmented, 121		
23	189	199	0.12	0.86	Earthworm, 124		
24	200	206	0.38	0.88	Arthropod, 7		
25	207	213	0.43	0.90	Linnaeus, 137		
26	214	229	0.53	0.92	Horse-shoe crab, 142		

	Origin	*Conclusion*	$\bar{B}_1$	$\bar{B}_2$	*Verbal Elements*
Secondary Span					
27	230	237	0.46	0.91	Foot, 146
28	238	247	0.25	0.85	Horse-shoe crab, 142
29	248	255	0.43	0.92	Variety, 161
30	256	263	0.55	0.91	Classes (of animals), 162
31	264	272	0.22	0.84	Arachnids, 164
32	273	281	0.44	0.91	Myriapod, 166
33	282	293	0.30	0.87	Crustaceans, 169
34	294	302	0.37	0.90	Echinoderms, 16
35	303	310	0.32	0.92	Sea urchin, 182
Decay Series:					
Real pulsed	210	213	0.25	0.89	
Real linear	102	105	0.58	0.95	
Gain Series:					
Artificial pulsed	62	67	0.40	0.90	
Symmetries:					
Real repeat, threefold	129	145	0.56	0.93	

DISTRIBUTION OF FUNDAMENTAL COEFFICIENTS

Interval	*Percentage of Coefficients Occurring in Each Interval*
0.000–0.095	37.09
0.096–0.195	0.64
0.196–0.295	3.22
0.296–0.395	4.83
0.396–0.495	9.35
0.496–0.595	15.48
0.596–0.695	15.48
0.696–0.795	0.00
0.796–0.895	0.96
0.896–1.000	12.58

Kinetogram of Transcript T-4

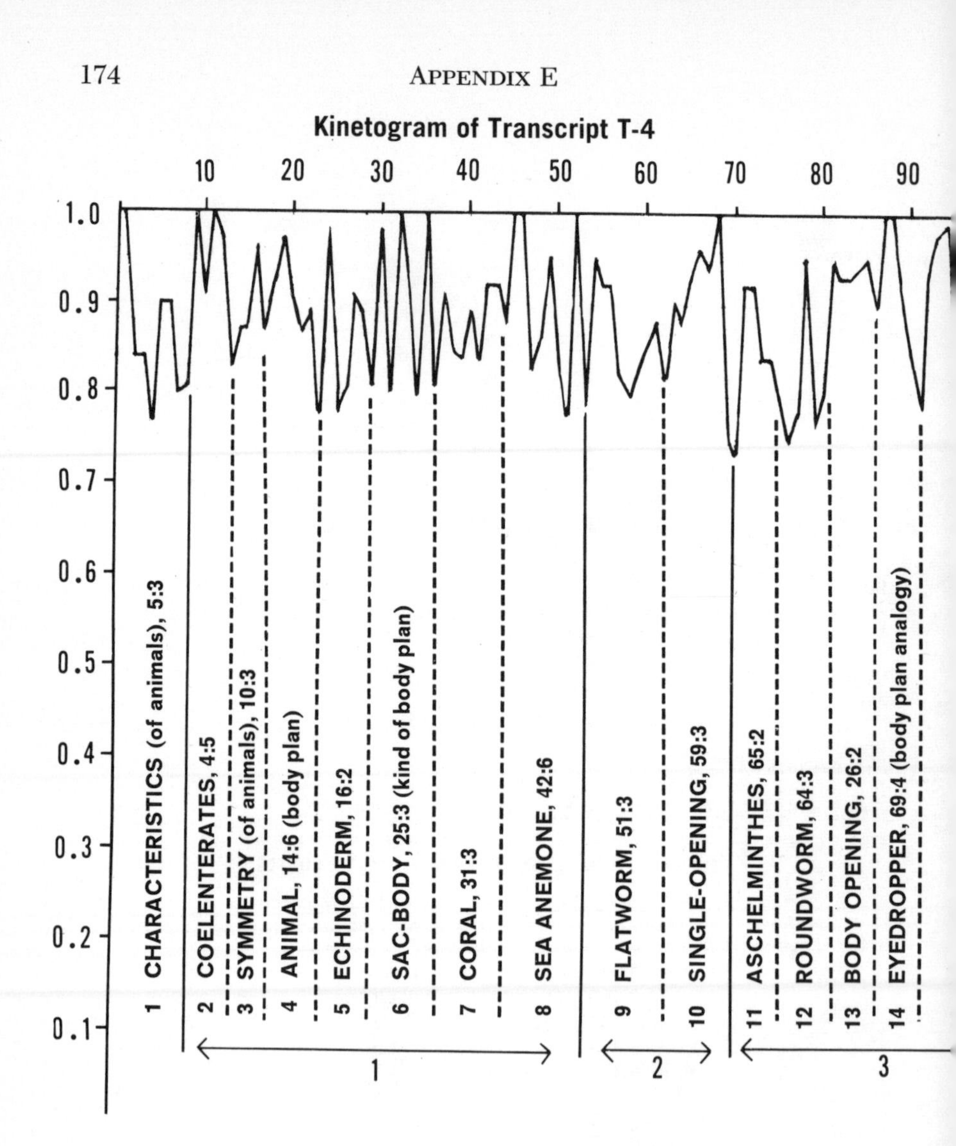

Kinetogram: T-4
(*overleaf*)

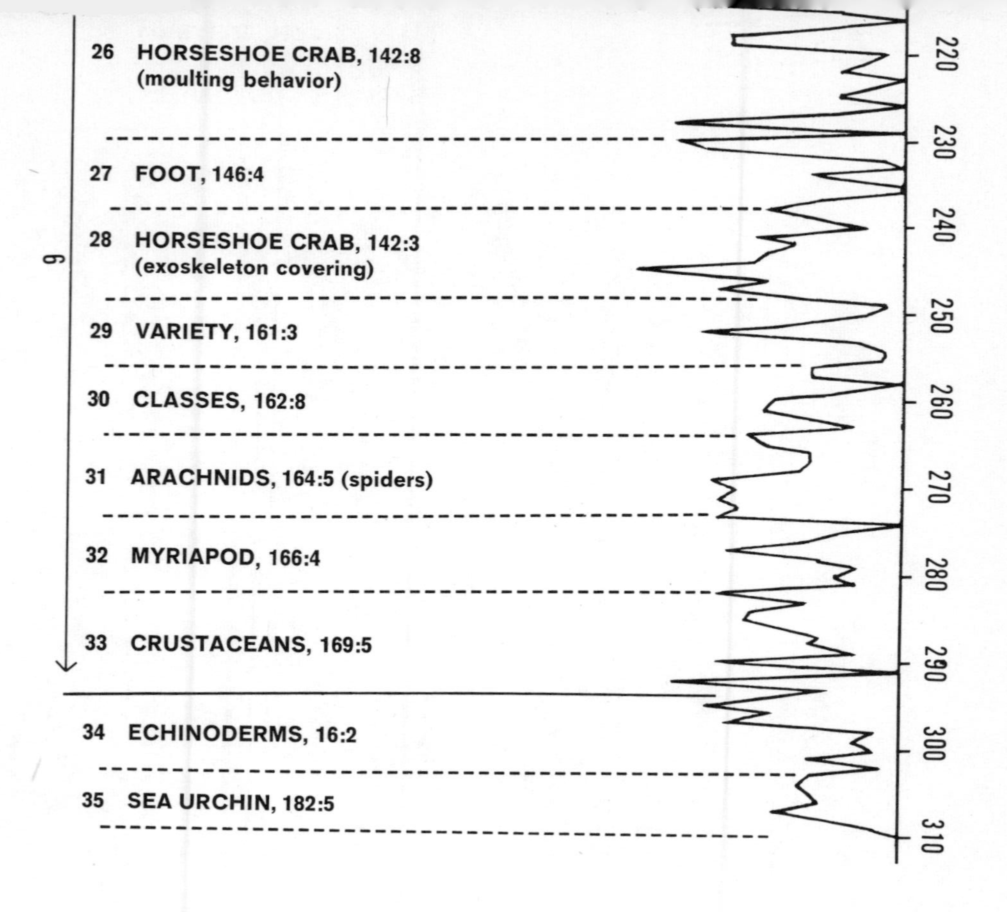
26 HORSESHOE CRAB, 142:8
(moulting behavior)
27 FOOT, 146:4
28 HORSESHOE CRAB, 142:3
(exoskeleton covering)
29 VARIETY, 161:3
30 CLASSES, 162:8
31 ARACHNIDS, 164:5 (spiders)
32 MYRIAPOD, 166:4
33 CRUSTACEANS, 169:5
34 ECHINODERMS, 16:2
35 SEA URCHIN, 182:5
6
220
230
240
250
260
270
280
290
300
310

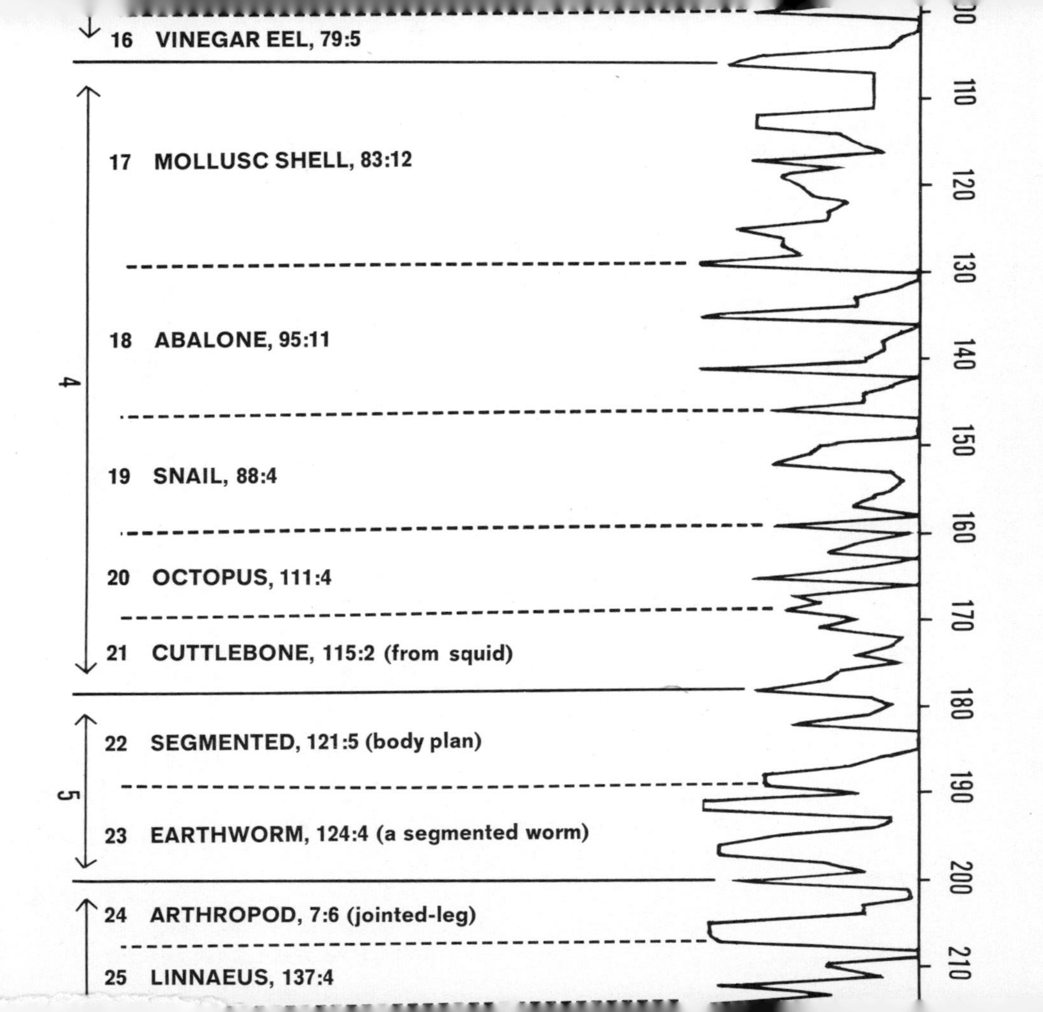
100
110
120
130
140
150
160
170
180
190
200
210
16 VINEGAR EEL, 79:5
17 MOLLUSC SHELL, 83:12
18 ABALONE, 95:11
19 SNAIL, 88:4
20 OCTOPUS, 111:4
21 CUTTLEBONE, 115:2 (from squid)
22 SEGMENTED, 121:5 (body plan)
23 EARTHWORM, 124:4 (a segmented worm)
24 ARTHROPOD, 7:6 (jointed-leg)
25 LINNAEUS, 137:4
4
5

Fundamental Coefficients for Transcript T-4

Discourse Unit	B_1	Discourse Unit	B_1	Discourse Unit	B_1
2	0.0	25	0.0	48	0.31
3	0.0	26	0.0	49	0.50
4	0.0	27	0.0	50	0.0
5	0.50	28	0.0	51	0.0
6	0.50	29	0.0	52	1.0
7	0.0	30	0.80	53	0.0
8	0.0	31	0.0	54	0.67
9	1.0	32	1.0	55	0.0
10	0.50	33	0.29	56	0.0
11	1.0	34	0.0	57	0.0
12	0.67	35	1.0	58	0.0
13	0.0	36	0.0	59	0.0
14	0.0	37	0.0	60	0.0
15	0.0	38	0.0	61	0.0
16	0.50	39	0.0	62	0.0
17	0.40	40	0.33	63	0.33
18	0.40	41	0.0	64	0.40
19	0.50	42	0.25	65	0.67
20	0.40	43	0.25	66	0.50
21	0.40	44	0.0	67	0.50
22	0.50	45	1.0	68	1.0
23	0.0	46	1.0	69	0.0
24	0.67	47	0.17	70	0.0

Discourse Unit	B_1	Discourse Unit	B_1	Discourse Unit	B_1
71	0.50	94	0.67	117	0.0
72	0.50	95	0.0	118	0.40
73	0.0	96	1.0	119	0.0
74	0.0	97	0.5	120	0.33
75	0.0	98	0.0	121	0.40
76	0.0	99	0.5	122	0.50
77	0.0	100	0.0	123	0.50
78	0.67	101	1.0	124	0.50
79	0.0	102	1.0	125	0.0
80	0.0	103	0.67	126	0.0
81	0.67	104	0.67	127	0.0
82	0.50	105	0.0	128	0.5
83	0.50	106	0.0	129	0.0
84	0.50	107	0.67	130	1.0
85	0.67	108	0.67	131	1.0
86	0.0	109	0.67	132	0.67
87	1.0	110	0.67	133	0.40
88	1.0	111	0.67	134	0.40
89	0.33	112	0.0	135	0.0
90	0.0	113	0.0	136	1.0
91	0.0	114	0.40	137	0.67
92	0.67	115	0.50	138	0.57
93	0.67	116	0.67	139	0.50

Discourse Unit	B_1	Discourse Unit	B_1	Discourse Unit	B_1
140	0.50	163	1.0	186	0.67
141	0.0	164	0.67	187	0.40
142	1.0	165	0.0	188	0.0
143	0.67	166	1.0	189	0.0
144	0.50	167	0.18	190	0.22
145	0.50	168	0.36	191	0.0
146	0.0	169	0.0	192	0.0
147	1.0	170	0.0	193	0.67
148	1.0	171	0.0	194	0.40
149	1.0	172	0.67	195	0.0
150	0.29	173	0.67	196	0.0
151	0.25	174	0.40	197	0.0
152	0.0	175	0.80	198	0.0
153	0.67	176	0.0	199	0.0
154	0.67	177	0.0	200	0.0
155	0.67	178	0.0	201	0.67
156	0.50	179	0.67	202	0.67
157	0.40	180	0.67	203	0.67
158	1.0	181	0.67	204	0.67
159	0.0	182	0.0	205	0.0
160	0.67	183	1.0	206	0.0
161	0.50	184	1.0	207	0.0
162	0.40	185	1.0	208	1.0

Discourse Unit	B_1	Discourse Unit	B_1	Discourse Unit	B_1
209	1.0	232	0.67	255	0.67
210	0.0	233	1.0	256	0.40
211	0.50	234	0.0	257	0.50
212	0.0	235	1.0	258	1.0
213	0.50	236	1.0	259	0.50
214	0.0	237	0.0	260	0.40
215	0.50	238	0.0	261	0.40
216	1.0	239	0.33	262	0.50
217	0.50	240	0.50	263	0.67
218	0.0	241	0.33	264	0.33
219	0.0	242	0.40	265	0.33
220	0.67	243	0.0	266	0.40
221	0.50	244	0.29	267	0.40
222	0.50	245	0.0	268	0.50
223	1.0	246	0.40	269	0.0
224	0.67	247	0.25	270	0.0
225	0.67	248	0.33	271	0.0
226	1.0	249	0.67	272	0.0
227	0.50	250	0.50	273	0.0
228	0.0	251	0.40	274	1.0
229	1.0	252	0.0	275	0.50
230	0.0	253	0.33	276	0.33
231	0.0	254	0.50	277	0.0

Discourse Unit	B_1
278	0.50
279	0.57
280	0.40
281	0.67
282	0.0
283	0.50
284	0.0
285	0.0
286	0.25
287	0.40
288	0.40
289	0.67
290	0.0
291	1.00
292	0.0
293	0.40
294	0.29
295	0.0
296	0.40
297	0.0
298	0.67
299	0.50
300	0.67
301	0.0
302	0.80
303	0.0
304	0.0
305	0.33
306	0.40
307	0.0
308	0.33
309	0.50
310	1.0

APPENDIX F

Kinetogram T-5 and Related Materials

Kinetogram Summary Table for Transcript T-5

Mean Fundamental Coefficient	Mean Weighted Coefficient
0.32	0.87
Total Number of Discourse Units	Total Frequency of Elements
211	483
Number of Primary Spans	Primary Span Mean Length
4	53
Number of Secondary Spans	Secondary Span Mean Length
23	9

	Origin	*Conclusion*	$\bar{B}_1$	$\bar{B}_2$	*Verbal Elements*	*Transition*	*TAC*
Primary Span							
1	1	28	0.37	0.88	Animal, 1 Specimen, 2		
2	29	89	0.40	0.87	Name, 29	NC	–
3	90	159	0.32	0.89	Animal, 1	NC	–
4	160	204	0.30	0.86	Chordates, 68	NC	–
Secondary Span							
1	1	10	0.40	0.86	Animal, 1 Mammal, 9 Bat, 11		
2	11	15	0.28	0.89	Insect, 13		
3	16	20	0.25	0.87	Preserved, 20		
4	21	28	0.44	0.90	Specimens, 2		
5	29	36	0.71	0.94	Name, 29		
6	37	47	0.29	0.86	Common name, 28		
7	48	63	0.24	0.83	Scientific name, 27		
8	64	85	0.34	0.86	Genus, 49		
9	86	89	0.40	0.84	Scientific name, 27		
10	90	108	0.40	0.89	Phylum, 62		
11	109	121	0.33	0.86	Chordate, 68 Vertebrate, 69		
12	122	128	0.07	0.83	Echinoderm, 75		
13	129	136	0.32	0.91	Mollusc, 77		
14	137	143	0.38	0.91	Earthworm, 93		
15	144	147	0.28	0.89	Hookworm, 96		
16	148	154	0.44	0.91	Flatworm, 98		
17	155	159	0.33	0.92	Coelenterate, 105		
18	160	166	0.39	0.88	Vertebrate, 69		
19	167	171	0.37	0.82	Solid piece, 111		
20	172	182	0.28	0.86	Gill slit, 114		
21	183	189	0.26	0.87	Spinal cord, 122		
22	190	204	0.19	0.86	Vertebrate, 69		
23	205	211	0.36	0.89	Characteristics, 8		

	Origin	*Conclusion*	$\bar{B}_1$	$\bar{B}_2$
Decay Series:				
Artificial linear	33	36	0.75	0.96
Gain Series:				
Artificial linear	37	41	0.18	0.86
	71	75	0.26	0.83

DISTRIBUTION OF FUNDAMENTAL COEFFICIENTS

Interval	*Percentage of Coefficients Occurring in Each Interval*
0.000–0.095	42.65
0.096–0.195	0.00
0.196–0.295	3.79
0.296–0.395	3.79
0.396–0.495	9.47
0.496–0.595	18.00
0.596–0.695	11.37
0.696–0.795	0.94
0.796–0.895	4.26
0.896–1.000	5.21

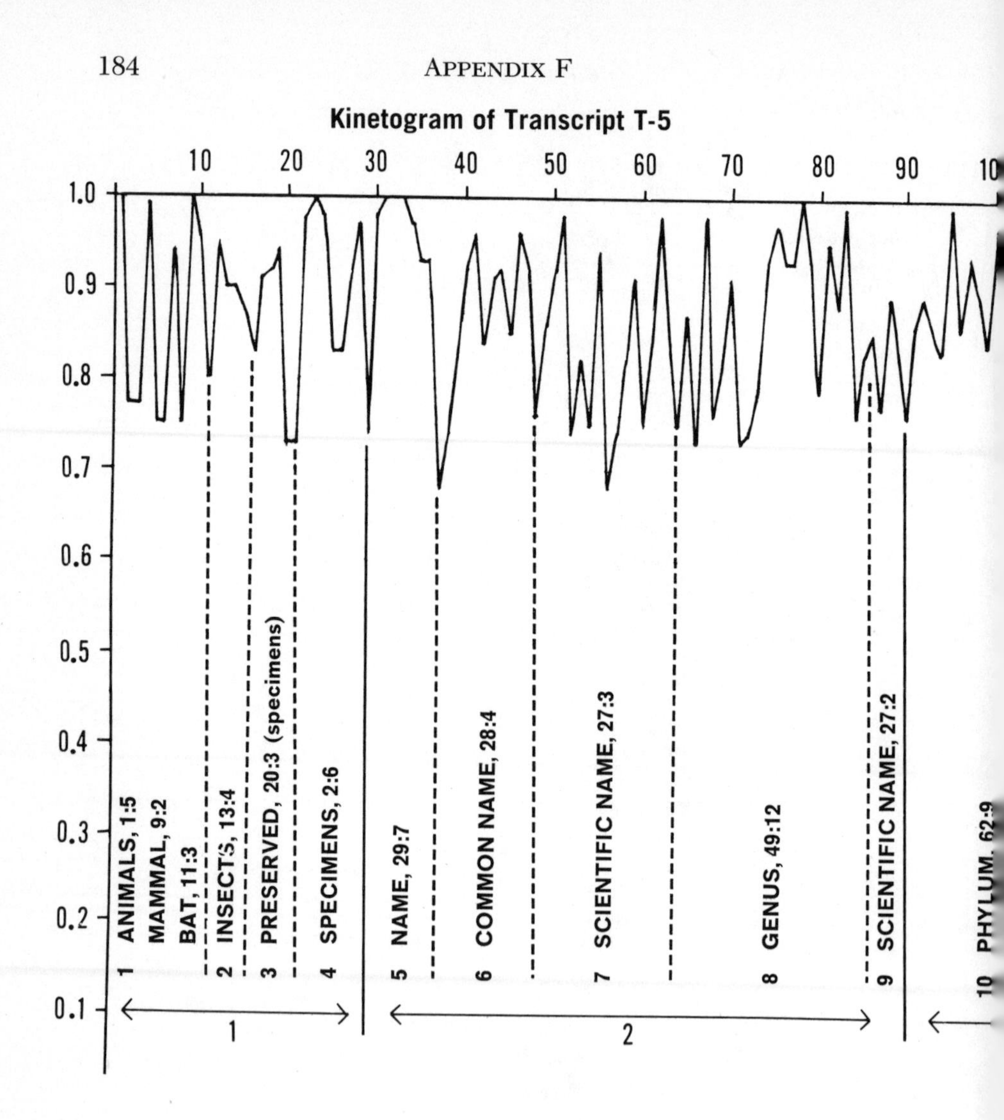
Kinetogram of Transcript T-5
1 ANIMALS, 1:5
MAMMAL, 9:2
BAT, 11:3
2 INSECTS, 13:4
3 PRESERVED, 20:3 (specimens)
4 SPECIMENS, 2:6
5 NAME, 29:7
6 COMMON NAME, 28:4
7 SCIENTIFIC NAME, 27:3
8 GENUS, 49:12
9 SCIENTIFIC NAME, 27:2
10 PHYLUM, 62:9
1
2

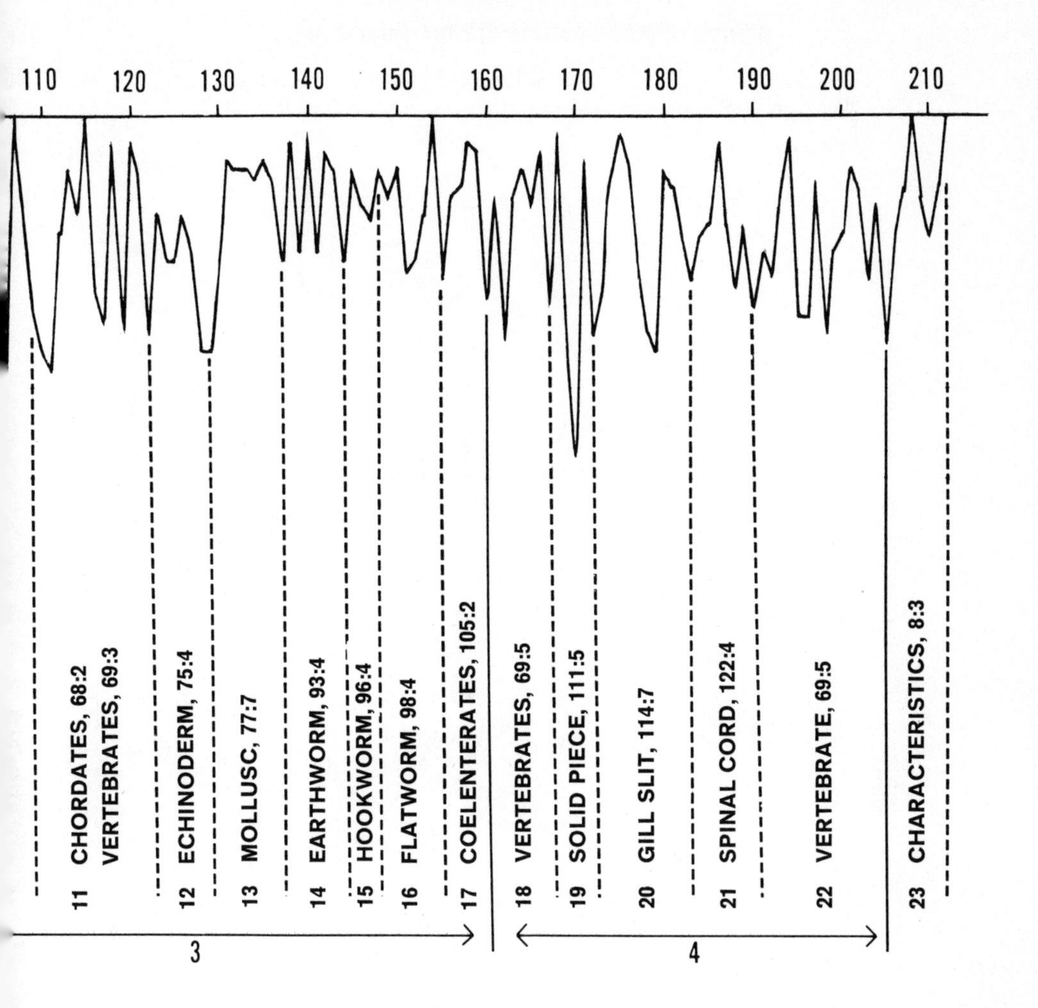
110
120
130
140
150
160
170
180
190
200
210
11 CHORDATES, 68:2
VERTEBRATES, 69:3
12 ECHINODERM, 75:4
13 MOLLUSC, 77:7
14 EARTHWORM, 93:4
15 HOOKWORM, 96:4
16 FLATWORM, 98:4
17 COELENTERATES, 105:2
18 VERTEBRATES, 69:5
19 SOLID PIECE, 111:5
20 GILL SLIT, 114:7
21 SPINAL CORD, 122:4
22 VERTEBRATE, 69:5
23 CHARACTERISTICS, 8:3
3
4

Fundamental Coefficients for Transcript T-5

Discourse Unit	B_1	Discourse Unit	B_1	Discourse Unit	B_1
2	0.0	23	1.0	44	0.40
3	0.0	24	0.67	45	0.33
4	0.67	25	0.0	46	0.57
5	0.0	26	0.0	47	0.57
6	0.0	27	0.40	48	0.0
7	0.67	28	0.80	49	0.40
8	0.0	29	0.0	50	0.40
9	1.0	30	0.67	51	0.80
10	0.75	31	1.0	52	0.0
11	0.0	32	1.0	53	0.0
12	0.40	33	1.0	54	0.0
13	0.50	34	0.67	55	0.75
14	0.50	35	0.67	56	0.0
15	0.0	36	0.67	57	0.0
16	0.0	37	0.0	58	0.29
17	0.40	38	0.0	59	0.40
18	0.50	39	0.0	60	0.0
19	0.33	40	0.40	61	0.0
20	0.0	41	0.50	62	0.80
21	0.0	42	0.0	63	0.0
22	0.67	43	0.40	64	0.0

Discourse Unit	B_1	Discourse Unit	B_1	Discourse Unit	B_1
65	0.50	88	0.50	111	0.0
66	0.0	89	0.0	112	0.40
67	0.80	90	0.0	113	0.67
68	0.0	91	0.50	114	0.40
69	0.0	92	0.57	115	1.0
70	0.40	93	0.29	116	0.0
71	0.0	94	0.33	117	0.0
72	0.0	95	0.80	118	0.67
73	0.0	96	0.0	119	0.0
74	0.50	97	0.0	120	0.67
75	0.80	98	0.0	121	0.50
76	0.50	99	0.0	122	0.0
77	0.50	100	0.67	123	0.50
78	1.0	101	0.50	124	0.0
79	0.50	102	0.67	125	0.0
80	0.0	103	1.0	126	0.0
81	0.67	104	0.40	127	0.0
82	0.57	105	0.29	128	0.0
83	0.80	106	0.0	129	0.0
84	0.0	107	1.0	130	0.0
85	0.0	108	0.50	131	0.67
86	0.0	109	0.0	132	0.29
87	0.0	110	0.0	133	0.44

Discourse Unit	B_1	Discourse Unit	B_1	Discourse Unit	B_1
134	0.33	157	0.0	180	0.67
135	0.50	158	0.0	181	0.57
136	0.33	159	0.50	182	0.0
137	0.0	160	0.0	183	0.0
138	0.67	161	0.50	184	0.40
139	0.0	162	0.0	185	0.33
140	0.80	163	0.50	186	0.67
141	0.0	164	0.67	187	0.40
142	0.67	165	0.50	188	0.0
143	0.50	166	0.57	189	0.0
144	0.0	167	0.0	190	0.0
145	0.40	168	0.67	191	0.33
146	0.33	169	0.44	192	0.0
147	0.40	170	0.22	193	0.50
148	0.50	171	0.50	194	0.80
149	0.50	172	0.0	195	0.0
150	0.50	173	0.22	196	0.0
151	0.29	174	0.40	197	0.67
152	0.29	175	0.67	198	0.0
153	0.0	176	0.50	199	0.0
154	1.0	177	0.0	200	0.0
155	0.0	178	0.0	201	0.0
156	0.50	179	0.0	202	0.0

Discourse Unit	B_1
203	0.0
204	0.50
205	0.0
206	0.50
207	0.50
208	1.0
209	0.50
210	0.0
211	0.0

APPENDIX G

Kinetogram T-6 and Related Materials

Kinetogram Summary Table for Transcript T-6

Mean Fundamental Coefficient	Mean Weighted Coefficient
0.32	0.79
Total Number of Discourse Units	Total Frequency of Elements
224	502
Number of Primary Spans	Primary Span Mean Length
4	36
Number of Secondary Spans	Secondary Span Mean Length
20	11

	Origin	*Conclusion*	$\bar{B}_1$	$\bar{B}_2$	*Verbal Elements*	*Transition*	*TAC*
Primary Span							
1	27	48	0.26	0.77	Radius, 22	C-2	0.6
2	100	127	0.26	0.79	Radius, 22 Ions, 54	NC	–
3	128	167	0.30	0.76	Electro-negative, 10	NC	–
4	168	219	0.41	0.78	Ionic bond, 1	NC	–
Secondary Span							
1	1	9	0.13	0.78	Force, 2		
2	10	17	0.23	0.84	Electro-negativity, 10		
3	18	26	0.48	0.82	Electron, 16		
4	27	37	0.31	0.77	Force, 2		
5	38	48	0.22	0.78	Increasing, 23 (atomic size)		
6	49	56	0.06	0.81	Area, 38		
7	57	72	0.46	0.85	Second shell, 44		
8	73	89	0.33	0.77	Outermost shell, 17		
9	90	99	0.30	0.79	Force, 2		
10	100	118	0.22	0.78	Increase, 23 Radius, 22		
11	119	127	0.35	0.83	Ion, 54		
12	128	138	0.30	0.77	Electro-negativity, 10		
13	139	151	0.29	0.72	Electron, 16		
14	152	158	0.32	0.76	Force, 2		
15	159	167	0.29	0.82	Halogen, 15		
16	168	184	0.50	0.82	Electron, 16		
17	185	202	0.35	0.76	Force, 2		
18	203	211	0.43	0.78	Sodium, 34		
19	212	219	0.32	0.78	Charge, 31		
20	220	224	0.13	0.81	Covalent bond, 63		

	Origin	*Conclusion*	$\bar{B}_1$	$\bar{B}_2$
Gain Series:				
Artificial				
linear	43	47	0.13	0.73
	51	54	0.13	0.82
	93	97	0.20	0.79
Decay Series:				
Real				
pulsed	181	188	0.34	0.77
Artificial				
pulsed	70	77	0.28	0.75
Symmetries:				
Mirror	210	216	0.43	0.84

DISTRIBUTION OF FUNDAMENTAL COEFFICIENTS

Interval	*Percentage of Coefficients Occurring in Each Interval*
0.000–0.095	46.42
0.096–0.195	0.00
0.196–0.295	4.46
0.296–0.395	4.46
0.396–0.495	8.03
0.496–0.595	11.60
0.596–0.695	12.50
0.696–0.795	0.00
0.796–0.895	3.12
0.896–1.000	8.92

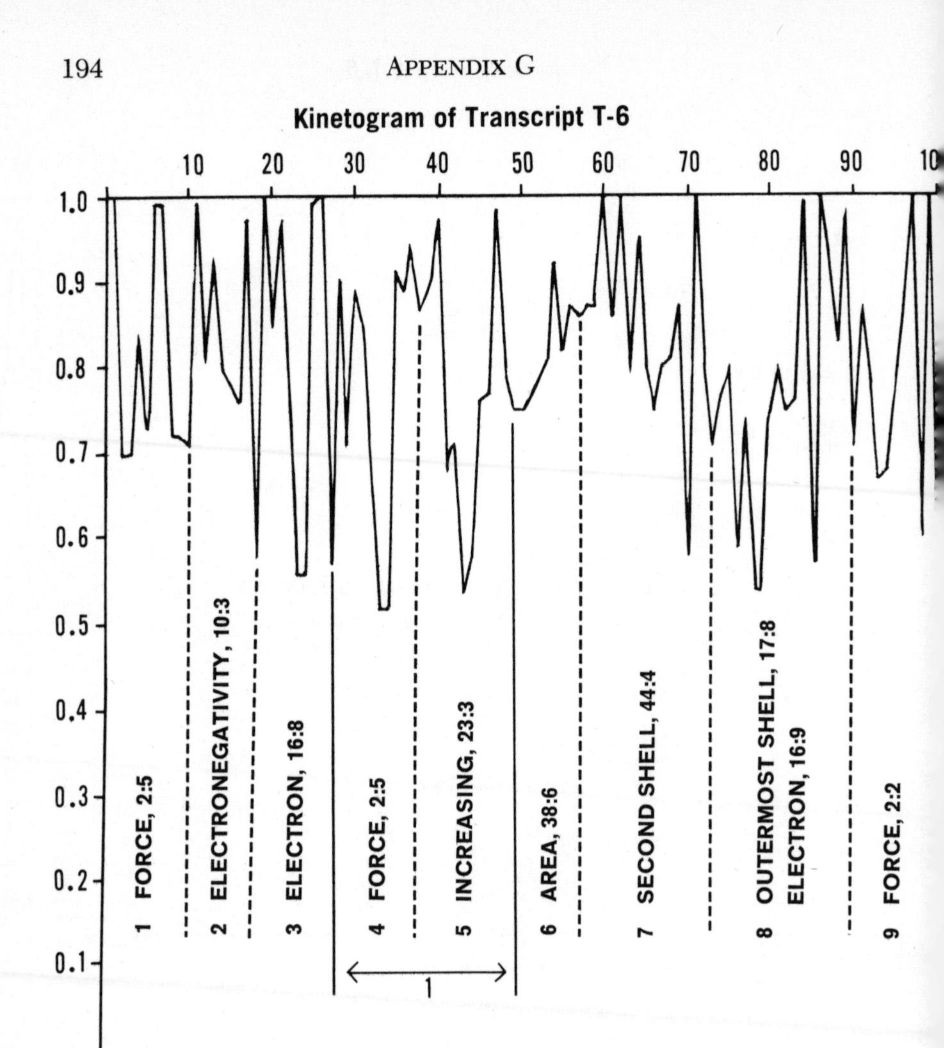
Kinetogram of Transcript T-6
10
20
30
40
50
60
70
80
90
1.0
0.9
0.8
0.7
0.6
0.5
0.4
0.3
0.2
0.1
1 FORCE, 2:5
2 ELECTRONEGATIVITY, 10:3
3 ELECTRON, 16:8
4 FORCE, 2:5
5 INCREASING, 23:3
6 AREA, 38:6
7 SECOND SHELL, 44:4
8 OUTERMOST SHELL, 17:8
ELECTRON, 16:9
9 FORCE, 2:2
1

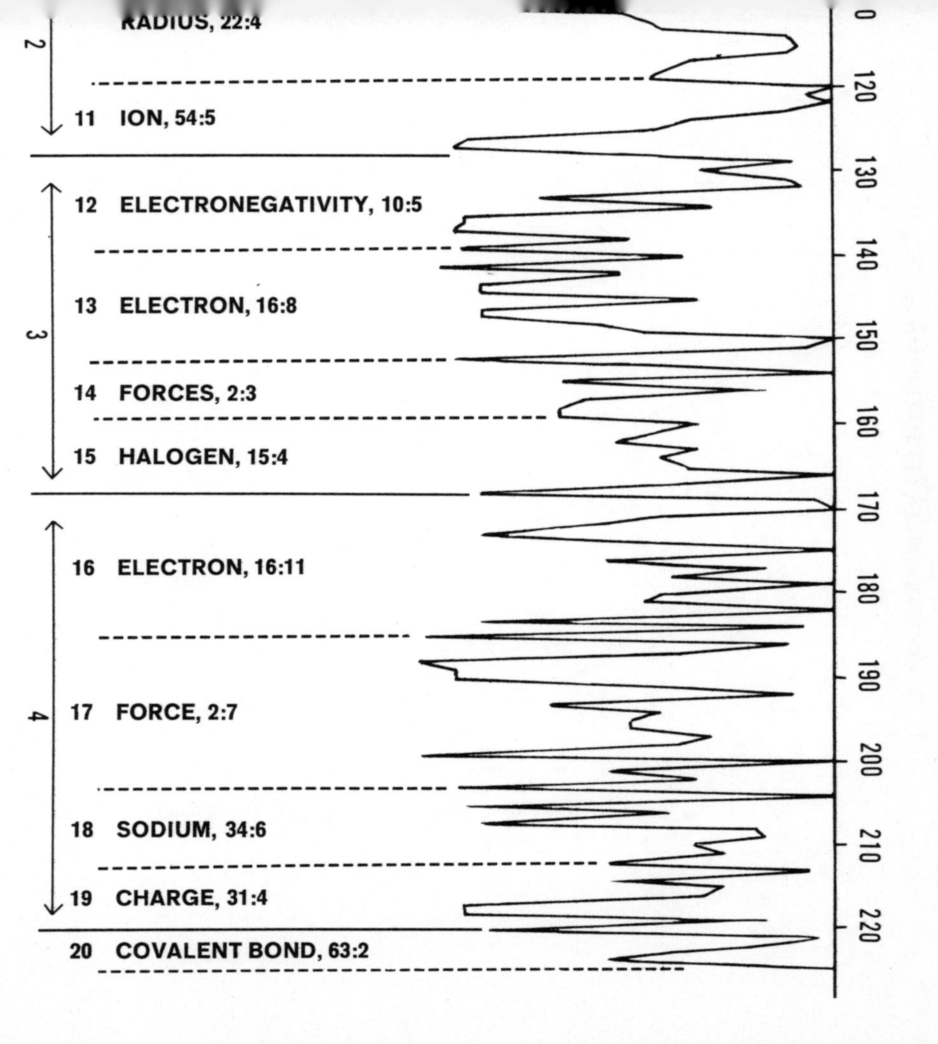
120
130
140
150
160
170
180
190
200
210
220
ADIUS, 22:4
11 ION, 54:5
12 ELECTRONEGATIVITY, 10:5
13 ELECTRON, 16:8
14 FORCES, 2:3
15 HALOGEN, 15:4
16 ELECTRON, 16:11
17 FORCE, 2:7
18 SODIUM, 34:6
19 CHARGE, 31:4
20 COVALENT BOND, 63:2
2
3
4

Fundamental Coefficients for Transcript T-6

Discourse Unit	B_1	Discourse Unit	B_1	Discourse Unit	B_1
2	0.0	23	0.0	44	0.0
3	0.0	24	0.0	45	0.0
4	0.0	25	0.67	46	0.0
5	0.0	26	1.0	47	0.80
6	0.67	27	0.0	48	0.0
7	0.67	28	0.40	49	0.0
8	0.0	29	0.33	50	0.0
9	0.0	30	0.50	51	0.0
10	0.0	31	0.40	52	0.0
11	0.67	32	0.40	53	0.0
12	0.0	33	0.0	54	0.50
13	0.50	34	0.0	55	0.0
14	0.0	35	0.50	56	0.0
15	0.0	36	0.29	57	0.0
16	0.0	37	0.57	58	0.67
17	0.67	38	0.40	59	0.50
18	0.0	39	0.50	60	1.0
19	1.0	40	0.67	61	0.50
20	0.50	41	0.0	62	1.0
21	0.80	42	0.0	63	0.50
22	0.33	43	0.0	64	0.67

Discourse Unit	B_1	Discourse Unit	B_1	Discourse Unit	B_1
65	0.50	88	0.33	111	0.0
66	0.40	89	0.80	112	0.0
67	0.0	90	0.40	113	0.0
68	0.0	91	0.29	114	0.67
69	0.67	92	0.33	115	0.67
70	0.0	93	0.0	116	0.67
71	1.0	94	0.0	117	0.0
72	0.0	95	0.0	118	0.0
73	0.33	96	0.0	119	0.0
74	0.40	97	1.0	120	1.0
75	0.50	98	0.0	121	0.67
76	0.0	99	1.0	122	1.0
77	0.0	100	0.0	123	0.50
78	0.0	101	0.40	124	0.0
79	0.0	102	0.0	125	0.0
80	0.0	103	0.0	126	0.0
81	0.0	104	0.0	127	0.0
82	0.40	105	1.0	128	0.0
83	0.40	106	0.40	129	0.67
84	0.80	107	0.33	130	0.50
85	0.0	108	0.0	131	0.67
86	1.0	109	0.0	132	0.67
87	0.67	110	0.0	133	0.29

Discourse Unit	B_1	Discourse Unit	B_1	Discourse Unit	B_1
134	0.50	157	0.40	180	0.50
135	0.0	158	0.33	181	0.0
136	0.0	159	0.0	182	1.0
137	0.0	160	0.62	183	0.0
138	0.0	161	0.22	184	0.80
139	0.0	162	0.40	185	0.0
140	0.29	163	0.33	186	0.67
141	0.0	164	0.0	187	0.29
142	0.40	165	0.0	188	0.0
143	0.0	166	1.0	189	0.0
144	0.0	167	0.0	190	0.0
145	0.50	168	0.0	191	0.57
146	0.0	169	0.80	192	0.50
147	0.0	170	1.0	193	0.0
148	0.40	171	0.29	194	0.50
149	0.50	172	0.29	195	0.29
150	1.00	173	0.0	196	0.29
151	0.67	174	0.50	197	0.67
152	0.0	175	1.0	198	0.57
153	0.0	176	0.40	199	0.0
154	1.0	177	0.67	200	1.0
155	0.0	178	0.33	201	0.33
156	0.50	179	1.0	202	0.50

Discourse Unit	B_1
203	0.0
204	1.0
205	0.0
206	0.50
207	0.0
208	0.67
209	0.67
210	0.40
211	0.67
212	0.0
213	0.80
214	0.0
215	0.67
216	0.44
217	0.0
218	0.0
219	0.67
220	0.0
221	0.67
222	0.0
223	0.0
224	0.0

Index

3 1303 00024 6117